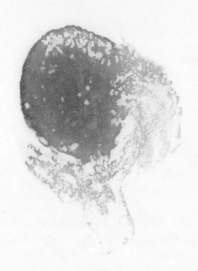

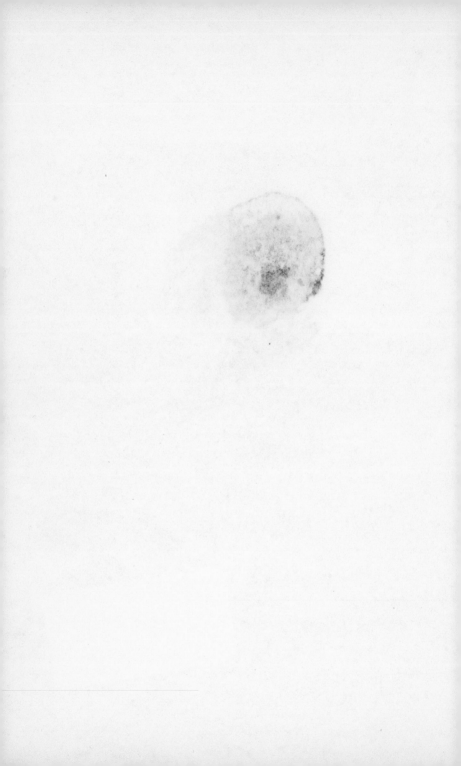

MAN AND COSMOS

Man and Cosmos

Scientific Phenomenology in Teilhard de Chardin

Paul Chauchard

PALM PUBLISHERS

1965
PALM PUBLISHERS   MONTREAL

Translated by George Courtright.
Original edition: *L'Etre humain selon Teilhard de Chardin*,
J. Gabalda et Cie, Paris, 1959.

Contents

Contents

*The hidden meaning of the world is wherever
we attain to vision of the diaphanous universe.*
TEILHARD DE CHARDIN

Our lost world is God the Father's holy creation.
URS VON BALTHASAR

*The natural sciences, once in lasting contact with
a philosophical realism, . . . can attain to a synthetic view of the visible world.*
PIUS XII

Introduction

WHAT is man? Traditional Christian humanism sees him as an incarnate spirit formed by God to His own image, with a nature made to be elevated to the supernatural and a soul betrothed to eternal life, but whom original and actual sin have so warped that it has taken the insertion of God into the human race to redeem him. Such is the concept of traditional Christian realist humanism, which, while it does not make man the supreme consideration, yet affirms in him an importance great enough to justify the Incarnation.

There appears to be a steadily increasing opposition to this concept, an opposition which seems to express unassailably the objective evidence of science and the arguments of materialism. As a chance product of biological evolution without real finality, man, who might have been produced almost anywhere else in the universe, is only a more perfect descendant in the animal series, where he must be ranked without possessing any peculiar nature of his own, and with no power of escaping death. His greatness is not in a personal relationship with God, but in the fact that, in him, complexified matter achieves consciousness and freedom, inventing a non-existent God or becoming capable in atheism of accepting the absurdity of his own condition.

Need the believer, then, take a defensive position and retreat before science? Is it true, as Marxists say, that it is enough to teach the scientific conception of man for the outdated myth of religion to disappear forever? Or is it possible to take a stand in some middle position and to distinguish two grounds in the study of man: that of matter, the body, as object of science, and that of spirit, as object of philosophy and faith? Once this was possible, but it is not so easy today, because, due to advances in the neurophysiology of the human brain, we are beginning to understand the cerebral mechanisms responsible for the specific constitution of the human psychism, for that which differentiates it from the animal psychism.

In our time, the materialist and atheistic uses of scientific discoveries concerning the material conditions of human spirituality, and a confusion of scientific definition and certitude with philosophical and religious definition and certitude, tend to make faith impossible, or, at the very least, of no interest to scientists whose mental habits have already turned them aside from a concept of the spiritual. It is also a time in which man's power over the world and himself have become formidable, a fact which calls for a further increase of spiritual resources. But in this very time, there is coming to be heard the voice of a Catholic priest who lived fully, even mystically, the faith of his Church. And this priest, a scientist, a paleontologist of world renown, and an expert in the evolutionary origins of man, not only felt uncramped in his faith by science, or obliged to separate within himself, like Pasteur, the scientist and the believer, but rather, without falling into a confusionist concordism, which makes an unscientific use of science, he showed us the perfect harmony, the convergence at a focal point, of the scientific conception of man—that very conception on which the propaganda of atheistic materialism is based—and the religious conception of traditional Catholicism. "I considered," Pierre Teilhard de Chardin tells us, "the abyss separating the intellectual world in which I found myself (the milieu of science), the language of which I understood, from the theological, the Roman Catholic, world, whose idiom I also knew. After the first shock of the idea that the latter could and must be as real as the former, I told myself that perhaps I was now ready, in speaking the language of the former, to make it legitimately express what the second preserves and repeats in words which have become incomprehensible to so many people."

What a providential stroke: that which serves to destroy faith can be made to confirm it! And indeed, there are many who can testify that the Teilhardian apologetic has helped them rediscover faith without their having to alter their scientific conception of the world, simply by coming to a better understanding of its true significance.

But Teilhard's work is much more than an apologetic at the practical service of traditional faith. If it does not always bring about conversion—that is the secret of the grace it opens the way to—it can make possible a union of all men around certain *common values* necessary for a concerted effort to build a joyful universe. It would make possible real toleration, a real lay activity. This does not mean that there is only relative truth or that every man has a truth of his own to be respected, but rather a recognition that there are certain scientifically objective aspects of truth accessible to all men. If men were united in a *natural ethic* based on what man is, on what he ought to do and what he ought not to do, instead of splitting up in utter relativism, they would then be able to reconcile the freedom of the act of faith in metaphysical terms with the added religious quickening in this natural ethic. Here the non-believer would see only rational necessity, without having to justify it otherwise than by scientific or psychological arguments.

Hence, there is a great importance and tremendous value in Teilhard's work for modern mankind, for atheist as well as for believer. For he has established a scientific humanism which, while novel, yet remains perfectly respectful of tradition. Teilhard is no crank thinker who evolves personal notions which one can accept or reject indifferently. He is an inspired precursor tracing out great vistas in a solid, scientific vision of the world, a vision of tomorrow, and demonstrating that, far from being philosophically materialist, as some think, the vision harmonizes with genuine Catholic faith, and not a faith compressed to fit the inner quality of his personal tenets. The problem which Teilhard takes up goes beyond personality. It is the problem of the relationship of science and philosophy, of science and Catholicism, in a world where science, now full-grown, rightly presses its claims to autonomy, to its own technology. This by no means implies that this science, this technology, wholly exhaust reality or that the autonomy contradicts dependence on a scheme of things which, though distinct, is not separate. The tragic conflict, which, since the birth of modern science, since Galileo, sets science and faith against each other in an utter confusionism—the Church, in defending faith, apparently opposing science, and the scientists or materialist philosophers, in extending science, wrongly opposing faith or seeming to—this conflict must now be resolved. The earth turns, therefore the Bible is wrong, says Galileo. The Bible cannot be wrong, therefore the earth does not turn, answers the Church. True and false, both. The earth does turn, as matter of scientific fact, but this is no concern of the Bible, the infallible inspiration of which bears solely on religious truth.[1]

The publication of Teilhard's work has now given his thought its full effect, or, rather, would give it effect if people would keep to the meaning which Teilhard intended. But no thinker has ever been so misunderstood. It is not that he lacks clarity; it is simply that his point of view is so new and so unusual that it shocks traditional thinking. People do not know how to classify it. For many scientists, the believers among them as well as the non-believers, this great synthesis, which goes beyond the customarily restricted point of view of scientific analysis, does not pertain to science at all. It is, they conclude, philosophical, qualificative, and, for the modern scientist, if not of no advantage at all, synonymous at least with want of accuracy, with the subjective. Atheistic scientists speak often of the distortion of science when it is put to the uses of faith, but they are forgetful of the fact that Huxley, an unbelieving evolutionist, describes the phenomenon of man in terms analogous to those of Teilhard, but without, of course, the latter's religious conclusions. Many scientists do believe in concordism, or in confusionism, and all too often they decline to bring their science into unity with their faith out of a desire to limit to the single ground of metaphysics the differences they have with their non-believing confreres.

On the other hand, too many philosophers still consider

[1] An essential difference between Galileo and Teilhard is that the latter introduces innovations only in the scientific realm.

Teilhard as though he belonged in their ranks, but he does not. Failing to comprehend the possibilities of science for understanding the world and man, a realm which, from the very beginning, was reserved to them, they accuse Teilhard of exchanging his competency as a scientist for that of a bad philosopher, the kind which Abbé Grenet, despite his impressive effort to sympathize and understand, calls "a philosopher without tools," that is to say, someone who makes the mistake of not using the conceptual instruments of philosophical research, who philosophizes without knowing how to, and who fails to give words their real meaning. The materialist philosophers feel that Teilhard denatures philosophy with idealism and the idealist philosophers, countless pupils of Plato, St. Augustine, and Descartes, see him as a fideist materialist who denies man his real, specific nature. Among the Thomistic philosophers, some, unfaithful to the spirit of their teacher, have turned idealist and absolutely oppose Teilhard, while others, more realist and understanding of his work, reproach him for not being a Thomist. Both forget that Thomist philosophy did not always keep in touch with science, indeed lost touch with science from the very beginning through the errors of nominalism, and through scholastic disputes divorced from the realities of growing scientific knowledge. Above all, they do not understand that there are two kinds of work necessary, each requiring specialization, each with a different technique: scientific *phenomenology,* or scientific *cosmology,* the scientific research which Teilhard calls *hyperphysics* and which requires a scientific mind directed toward the material but open to philosophy; and *ontological* cosmology, or metaphysics, the true philosophy of the sciences, which

14

remains strictly the work of the philosophers, though it exacts some scientific inquiry of them.

Again, Teilhard has been blamed for not being a man who knows everything about everything, when we ought rather to give him credit for his refusal to go beyond the limits of his own field. He has never said that he intended to give a *summa* of philosophical and theological thought. When *The Phenomenon of Man* first came out, and many times afterward, he stated his intention of remaining within the limits of phenomenology —"nothing but the phenomenon, yet the whole phenomenon." We will shortly see what he understands by that, and how it involves a new scientific phenomenology bringing us the scientific aspect of being, and which is, therefore, a phenomenology which refuses to remain on the surfaces of things, but is *introspective, ontological,* and *normative.* "But," it may be objected, "even if we admit, contrary to the verdict of classical science and philosophy, that such a phenomenology is true scientific work, there is no doubt that Teilhard goes too far. His vision of evolution converges on an 'Omega Point,' and he does not conceal that this involves God." However, anyone who remains within the confines of the "phenomenon of man" and yet neglects "the divine milieu" impoverishes and seriously mutilates Teilhardian thought.

Still, we must not conclude from all of this that, in confusionism or concordism, Teilhard turned philosopher and theologian while thinking to remain a scientist. It must not be inferred that he started from science and then developed a new theology opposed to the old idea. It is not his claim to repeal all the old notions in the field of philosophy and faith. Nor did he intend to work out all the philosophical and religious consequences of his scientific phenomenology. That is the business of the philosophers and the theologians, once they understand the position of this phenomenology. Teilhard and the scientists have no secret desire to replace them. However, any scientist with religious beliefs, who works out a phenomenolgy, which some might think of as materialist in its concern with material and organic conditions, infrastructures, owes it to himself to declare its agreement with his faith. Had Teilhard remained within the strict confines of science, precisely where the non-believers are able to follow him, no one would have failed to charge him once more with materialism or pantheism, against which, of course, he must explicitly defend himself.

But this is not all. No one who scientifically considers the whole phenomenon, especially if his faith has sensitized him, can fail to notice from the very design of the phenomenon certain aspects which, from the metaphysical and theological points of view, are especially in evidence. Does not the personalization-directed process of evolution, ever mounting toward the "Omega phenomenon," logically imply, without any technical philosophizing, that this Omega phenomenon is a personal God? that the dialectic of love in creation immerses us in the divine milieu? How can we deal with the whole phenomenon while neglecting this aspect of it? The Teilhardian picture thus includes whatever in religious phenomenology is peculiarly accessible to and in harmony with the vision of science, not for the privilege of a limited field, but to throw new light on certain aspects of faith all too commonly overlooked.

From this point of view, Teilhard's thought requires that one have, like him, a living faith—not the technical elaborations of professional theology, but the elementary, dogmatic knowledge which every believer needs. The believer who accuses Teilhard of neglecting so essential an aspect of faith is in error. Teilhard believes just as the other, but for him this was a definitely settled matter, and he had nothing new to say about it from the viewpoint of his phenomenology. The believer who infers from that that Teilhard alters religion is completely mistaken. As for the non-believer, he ought to know very well that, if Teilhard does away with his prejudices against faith, he is *leading him to the catechism, not taking the catechism's place.* He is not at all, as some have thought, some kind of preacher of a religion purged of traditionalism and adapted to the world of science. Teilhard changes nothing in Christian philosophy or dogma. The new point of view from which he sees these and which does not abrogate the classical point of view, only makes for a better understanding of them along the lines of *genuine progress,* that is to say, *of steady, self-fulfilling development.* Far from abolishing classical conceptions (which actually have their rightful place in his view), Teilhard thus develops certain aspects of theological reality which are somewhat overlooked but still profitable to us. If he were to say that these aspects are the only truths, he would be wrong. If, on the contrary, one puts these aspects, as he personally did, back into the integrity of the faith, truth becomes the more complete. This is why, while recognizing the evil of original and personal sin beyond any question, he takes a particular hold of the more general aspect of the evil inherent in creation. In his vision of the future, he emphasizes what ought *normally* to be, and not those disturbances which human sin introduces, and which make us falter in our natural development.

One of his readers, attentive especially to the apparent divergence between Teilhard and the traditional stand, once wondered if Teilhard should not be sent to the stake. If we did that, it would be by a sort of defense reaction due to our having understood nothing of him, of the essentially scientific stamp of his work, which ends by flowing out on the realms of faith and remaining there deliberately unfinished. However, it is so easy not to understand Teilhard with the same uncomprehendingness which those of his admirers, who set him up as opposed to his own Church, have in common with those of his opponents who, themselves joining the very ranks of orthodoxy in their opposition, pass sentence on him!

So much the more easily does Teilhard often appear poet, prophet, and mystic, and the more easily do these three characteristics seem to resist the commonplace mind of classical science and rationalism. We shall see, indeed, that this mystic who rediscovers God in the "diaphaneity" of a world whose surfaceness wearies him; that this poet who has, in his vision, intuitively grasped the thing which science only confirms for him; that this prophet who deduces objectively that which will be from the meaning of that which has been—we shall see that these three things are one in this scientist, in his unity of thought.

The polemic which sets Teilhardians and anti-Teilhardians at odds these days comes from confusion and total lack of understanding. And all this when only a little light needs to be shed in order to see that Teilhard's work is—not dangerous, but, on the contrary, perfectly practical. Traditionalist philosophers might then come away from a discussion of his meaning better prepared to carry on their own proper work, to develop, as philosophers and theologians, his scientific thought, and thus assist the progress of philosophy and theology while readying his thought to explain the scientific vision of the world. It is noteworthy that all the elements for evolving a modern philosophy of science are in traditional Thomistic philosophy. No change is required in its principles. All that is needed is an attempt at adaptation.

If we now put ourself at the service of Teilhardian thought, we do so, not so much as a follower of Teilhard de Chardin, but as a biologist,[1] a "believer" like him, and as a man trained in a different science, the neurophysiology of the brain, which has a great deal to tell us objectively about the material conditions of the spiritual in human life. By profession, the neurophysiologist is bound to regard the philosophical problems concerning the relation of soul and body. We have, therefore, a personal, professional obligation to witness to Teilhard and to join him in his defense of the scientific phenomenology of the phenomenon of man in an evolving creation; to corroborate the fact that this is not a philosophical question, but rather a philosophical aspect of scientific work; and to show that nothing in this phenomenology contradicts traditional concepts. Here the neurophysiologist has a double advantage over the paleontologist. On the one hand, he has a better grasp of the "within of things," because his concern is with the cerebral mechanism of human interiority. On the other hand, wholly immune to the

[1] Not at all as a philosopher, but as one open to philosophy and with due respect for its rights.

19

temptation of the idealist to separate body and soul, or to make an absolute division between man and the brute animal (Descartes's mistake), he feels himself profoundly in harmony with the realist philosophy which St. Thomas Aquinas borrowed from Aristotle and rectified, and which, also, according to Tresmontant, is the metaphysics immanent in biblical thought. When one has pondered with Sertillanges on the surprising analogies in Claude Bernard and St. Thomas Aquinas, one feels very much impelled to clarify the agreement between scientific phenomenology and Thomistic philosophy with regard to their points of view and their different methods. This would make possible, through an abatement of scientific passions, that work-force comprised of scholar, philosopher, and theologian which Rabut so rightly insists on, not for the purpose of debating the letter of Teilhardian thought, but of drawing together a unified cosmology from the two tributaries, upper and lower respectively, of scientific phenomenology and ontological metaphysics. Here we must say how much this book owes to the philosophical criticisms of Fathers d'Armagnac, Catalan, and Foulquié, and of Abbé Grenet and Abbé Daujat, all of whom have been most helpful.

We shall begin, then, by recalling the nature and the primary data of the scientific phenomenology of the world and of man. Then we shall look into its relationship with religion and Thomistic philosophy. We shall follow this with a consideration of certain consequences of scientific phenomenology, which, as a *realist* vision, encourages every assistance to an understanding of the meaning of evil, and which, on the other hand, denies the opposite errors of Pelagian optimism and Manichaean pessimism, both contrary to Christian thought. We shall thus see how wrong it is to tax Teilhard with a systematic optimism neglectful of sin and human freedom. We shall see how, on the contrary, scientific phenomenology can lead to a *resacralization* of a world which classical science has profaned, clearly showing that, in the divine milieu, nature and supernature, each keeping within its own dimensions, are yet not to be dissociated.

I

Scientific Phenomenology,
Its Nature and Meaning

A New Field in Scientific Thought

THE full implications of Teilhard's use of the phrase "scientific phenomenology" will not, perhaps, be evident until our final chapter. And though the actual terminology employed may matter very little, yet we must begin all the same by being as unambiguous as possible. Scientific phenomenology is not the phenomenology of the philosophers or of metaphysics. It is a process of synthetic reflection aimed at describing and understanding the world by starting from a unification of the data of the various experimental sciences, which are the study of natural phenomena. It is, withal, a kind of reflection which, being neither that in the common meaning of the word nor that of the philosopher using his conceptual methods, his own principles of inquiry, is the kind used by the scientist who means to stay within the territory of science. It is thus a new field in scientific thought. Certainly, if one is going to devote himself to it, he must have the synthetic spirit and have grasped the fact that the business of science is not limited merely to expert analysis of the various aspects of reality. Such limitation borders on total

22

ignorance of the whole meaning of reality and is very like becoming so excited about the individual bricks of a building that one forgets completely the superstructure. Nothing in this involves being a philosopher, nor, especially, does it mean technical philosophizing. It means only that the scientist is interested in the over-all meaning of his work. Unfortunately, the mathematical and physical sciences have accustomed us to believe that being objective in science means isolating oneself in a precise analysis of material detail, in reducing something to a mathematical formula. Contrariwise, the biologist, though he may at times succumb to the temptation to lose himself in detail, the more so since his progress depends on a quest for exact detail, keeps ever before his mind the idea of the whole. For he knows, with Bernard, that detail is of importance in biology only by reference to the organism of which it is a part, and to the degree that it benefits the functional good of that organism taken in its integrated unity. It was a wise precept— never to forget the organism, the whole—which Bernard gave to physiologists and doctors, not thereby to stir them into becoming philosophers, but that they might perform minutely a scientific work which no one else could do in their place. Bernard, some critics have said, was not a philosopher. But if not, undeniably he was a scientist who often took sides against philosophers. He was a scientist with a philosophical mind, who was able to follow his consideration of phenomena through to the end, but consideration which was not formulated as a conceptual scheme, but which, within a physiological framework, was directed to the discovery of the material laws of organic integration. Similarly, when he considered the methods

23

of science, he did so not as an epistemologist, but as a technician concerned with criticism and improvement of his instrument. We should, then, to some degree, associate the founder of the science of physiology with this spirit of over-all reflection on the meaning of the scientific phenomenon which is so characteristic of Teilhard. To be sure, Bernard confined himself strictly to the organic order, and was unprepared for a physiology of the brain sufficiently developed to make possible, as he would have wanted, an understanding of the real, organic dimension of the "within of things." We see again, moreover, and the more so in the case of the non-believing Bernard, the same ambiguities as in Teilhard. What is he really thinking? Is he a materialist nervous of going the whole way in his thought? A bashful vitalist? Not really, for as a realist experimenter, Bernard never ceased to direct severe criticism toward both materialists and spiritualists, that is, the vitalists. Sertillanges, the thinker who best understood Bernard, describes for us, in fact, how the physiologist came to reject the errors of mechanism and idealism. And this, though he was unaware of it, brought him to a *realist* position in complete accord with Thomistic philosophy. Bernard's is the first example of a modern scientific phenomenology debouching on Thomism, a philosophy which, from its Aristotelian beginnings, always concentrated especially on biological problems.

An example taken from the history of the neurophysiology of the brain will provide us with a good indication of the intent of scientific phenomenology at the end of the nineteenth century. At that time, there was hope of localizing consciousness and thought in the form of material substances stored in the productor neurones. Brain phenomena and psychological processes

24

were hardly differentiated at first, and failure was forestalled only by a sensible decision to limit experimentation, as Pavlov did, to a strictly physiological analysis of reflexes and nerve impulses, and of the switching of these through alternate stimulation and inhibition. The vocabulary of psychology was proscribed, which was allowable enough, except that the experimenters persisted in the conclusion that, if neurophysiology did not encounter consciousness, it was because it was an unimportant epiphenomenon. The error, of course, was that they, the experimenters, were unable to believe that consciousness has a physiological aspect and that there is something beyond the physiological, and could only believe, therefore, that the physiological, which is always to be found in any creature with a body, exhausts the content of its reality.

The Gestaltists, however, disagreed. Only the over-all functioning of the brain, taken as a whole, they said, matters, though for the most part neurophysiologists paid little heed, particularly where the Pavlovian conditioned-reflex methods were being tested. The Gestaltists had created a "mythic" physiology, which is a fine example of what a scientific phenomenology would be if it were written by philosophers, and the neurophysiologists were right to complain. But the very course of their science, the progress of their experiments on the animal and the human brain—the organ of behavior and thought—obliged them to note that the brain was not simply the seat of independent reflexes, but that it had an integrated unity of operation. They returned, therefore, to the teachings of Bernard, to a complete phenomenology of the brain, including thought and consciousness, but a physiological phenomenology of the whole which met the desire of the Gestaltists to take account of any fresh material which the whole might adduce. At the same time, it met the desires of the physiologists, who affirmed that this fresh material depends on the physiological integration of elementary processes as adduced by classical neurophysiology. Pavlov was not wrong to have studied the laws of conditioned reflexes, the essential mechanism of cerebral operations at the service of thought; nor to have determined the way in which the phantasm of the world, taken as an ordinary cerebral construct—or "word"—is organized in our cerebral interiority. His mistake was to have neglected the cerebral aspect of interiority, the physiology of consciousness. Had he not backed away from this metaphysical concept, he would have had the elements for an understanding of how, in the brain, there is not only the phantasm of the external world, but also the phantasm of the self, and of how that phantasm has a special role in the cerebral whole and guarantees the possibility of the personalization of sense impulses and motor commands, thereby guaranteeing also consciousness of sensation and willing.

Today, all physiologists are concerned with the neurophysiology of consciousness, because they have had to acknowledge that cerebral physiology differs in the conscious and the unconscious state. Yet, many still hesitate to recognize the full scope of physiology. Scarred as they are by the idealist philosophy of Descartes as Sherrington accepts it, they see consciousness as a spiritual process separated from the organism on which it acts. For them, subjectivity appears to be by nature inaccessible to science. But this is true only when there is question of subjectivity as such.

The philosopher, reflecting on his subjectivity, will of course, study his subjectivity in a philosophical way, that is to say, conceptually. The psychologist, in turn, will act either like a traditional philosopher and agree to study subjectivity, or, in a scientific spirit, he will choose to limit himself strictly to an objective analysis of behavior, while declining to have anything to do with subjectivity. If any progress in psychology results from this abstention, there is nonetheless a sizable loss to knowledge concerning the specific nature of the human psychism. Thus, objectivity of this kind seriously mutilates the animal psychism, the uppermost levels of which are in danger of being ignored because of the desire to see it only as a reflex-machine, and because of neglect of the real scope of interiority, the seat of behavior control. We are reduced to the "animal-machine," the "man-machine."

Only by thinking along neurophysiological lines can we progress. The neurophysiologist who is willing to turn from his experiments in order to consider the fact that the cerebral mechanisms which he is analyzing are those of his own brain and vouch for his thought, his reflective powers, his interiority, his personal subjectivity—no need here for philosophy, but only of common sense to grasp this truth—will not thereby be philosophizing, but only be asking himself, *within the limits of his special field,* how neurophysiology gives an objective account of all this subjectivity. He will then see that willing reflection on the matter is enough to clarify some very important questions, which would never be resolved if he refused to reflect, as a technician, on his own interiority. Yet, he must not make the mistake of thinking that this cerebral aspect of interiority

27

exhausts the question. Having explained it for the philosopher, who has no reason to deny it, he will wisely leave the latter to do his proper work: to give an *ontological* explanation of the meaning of these cerebral phenomena of which he had disclosed the neurophysiological dimension.

The work of the neurophysiologist, leading to a reëvaluation of the introspective process—which experimental psychology, supported by neurophysiology, must always take into account— is not limited to human interiority. The neurophysiologist, having grasped the relationship uniting interiority and cerebral complexity, disposes of one objective degree of interiority and animal subjectivity—the degree of development of higher nervous activity—and is then ready to give objective counsel to the zoöpsychologist in the latter's difficult studies in animal behavior of the roles of consciousness, comprehension, and control with respect to the innate reflexes of instinct or the automatic reactions of training.

Thus we begin to understand better what the *whole* phenomenon means for Teilhard: accepting the data, not of philosophy, but of common reflection, and inquiring whether science confirms them and how it explains them. We see that, for this task, there is need, not of philosophers, but of scientific experts, the more so because, far from being a matter of theoretical speculation, science must conduct these practical experiments if it is to progress. Teilhardian phenomenology does not lose us in a cloud of concepts. It demands experimental progress. It is *heuristic*.

In the end, the name given to this synthesis of the sciences matters little, provided we recognize the fact that we are dealing with a field which belongs exclusively to the scientists, where specialists must outdo themselves while yet remaining within their own domain, and which is of the utmost importance for the future of civilization. The word "phenomenology" clearly indicates an intention to stick to the descriptive aspects of events, which, far from obliging us to remain superficial, external, implies an obligation not to overlook the interior aspect of phenomena; hence, the apt qualification of the insignificant epithet *"introspective."* The disadvantage of the word "phenomenology" is that, too often, philosophers mean thereby precisely a superficial, psychological phenomenology of the spiritual in the content of consciousness, a phenomenology even more widely divided, as we shall see, from metaphysics than from scientific phenomenology. There is, besides, a striking relationship between Gestaltism, so contrary to a real cerebral phenomenology, and philosophical phenomenology. Teilhard himself saw the difficulty. "I realize," he wrote in 1953, "that my 'phenomenology' is not that of Husserl and Merleau-Ponty. But where to find another word to define a *Weltanschauung* based on the study of the development of the phenomenon? One is really forced to use the word 'evolution' of theories widely differing one from another. . . . Indeed, if I rightly understand, the 'phenomenologists' honor themselves wrongly with that title, to the degree that they ignore, as they seem to, one of the most essential dimensions of the phenomenon: that it is not only to be perceived by an individual consciousness, but (in addition and at the same time) is to indicate to this particular consciousness that it is included in a universal process of 'noögenesis.' I do not understand how one can call himself a 'phenomenologist' and write entire books without at least mentioning, without even naming cosmogenesis and 'evolution'! Really, Sartre and Merleau-Ponty (and the other philosophers at the Sorbonne) are still living in a pre-Galilean universe."

In order to make clear that his work, though it converged on the philosophical, was not philosophical or metaphysical, Teilhard defined it impartially as a *general physics,* a *hyperphysics.* Here we must understand physics in the sense of a science of nature, a hyperphysics essentially biological. Now, it is existence itself, considered as the object of an autonomous science, which Grenet contests. For him, the aims of hyperphysics, its problems, its friends and its enemies, indicate it to be a metaphysics, the more so because it proposes to reconcile materialism and spiritualism. In other words, to be on a level with these metaphysical matters is perforce to be philosophy. Such a judgment grossly misunderstands the specific character of the Teilhardian vision.

Of course, scientific phenomenology, hyperphysics, or again, more simply, scientific cosmology (to distinguish from the philosophical cosmology wedded to science) has a purpose analogous to metaphysics: it is intimately concerned with the study of the whole of reality. But we must recognize that where the classical approach to being, which remains the specific approach, is metaphysics with its own conceptual methods of inquiry, the goal which Teilhard proposes is the creation of a new approach to being, considered from another point of view, by means of study having nothing to do with philosophy. That is to say, a *scientific approach.* It deals with the *material* aspect, the *organic* aspect of being, with its infrastructure, and, by reason of the unity of being, this aspect opens out for us on horizons embracing the totality of being, that aspect of it which is *material being* and not

30

just the material part of being. If hyperphysics seeks to reconcile materialists and spiritualists, it is not through a resolve of their essential philosophical differences. Rather, it is chiefly on the ground of their "irrealist" differences regarding the scientific aspect of being. When science has helped to eliminate the last trace of mechanist materialism and separatist idealism; when all philosophers accept the *unity* of being, whether or not they distinguish as inseparable, in this life, two metaphysical principles or believe in an essential unity—and the minds of Thomism and dialectical materialism[1] meet here, then many a sterile argument will vanish, and many an obstacle to faith, now apparently enormous, will shrink to size. But Teilhard goes much further. He is convinced that, by pushing phenomenology and hyperphysics to the utmost, one can bring the non-believer who wants to be logical to recognize that the full dimension of the phenomenon compels him, by reason of its design, to take into account the full specific nature of the human person and of a personal God of love. It is only the question of the scientific argument in support of faith which is raised here, and we shall not discuss it now. We would simply show that, even at this higher level, hyperphysics does not become metaphysics, but remains a scientific contemplation of the world. The view of God in which it terminates is not the metaphysical view or a distortion of the metaphysical God, or a self-deception concealing a path to the metaphysical. Rather, it sees the face of God appearing through his creation like a watermark; it is a scientific vision, so to speak, reserved for the man who *knows how to see* deeply

[1] Satisfactory enough from the scientific standpoint when faithful to its methodological and heuristic principles, but very inadequate from the philosophical standpoint.

enough. It is a vision, therefore, which is quite different from all false, superficial concordisms, and which remains scientific in the company of the deepest faith. This does not hinder the approach by classical paths to the real theological or mystical ways of seeing God. The whole problem rests in knowing in what degree properly philosophical reflection and faith are or are not prerequisites for an approach to this scientific aspect. But this is not at all to do away with the existence of the possibility of this approach, which only those who have found it are sure of. In any case, it is only a matter of elementary, philosophical reflection, and this does not necessitate being a professional philosopher.

We see, then, the great danger of confusion if we do not grasp clearly the reality of the specific nature of Teilhardian scientific phenomenology. "Classical" scientists and philosophers alike have accused Teilhard of being, unwittingly, a metaphysician. He was not.

The confusion threatens from two sides. Thus, the scientist may refuse to perform an essential part of his work on the pretext of wishing to avoid any philosophizing, and the philosopher see in Teilhard a bad philosopher and complain about his unsatisfactory use of philosophical concepts, such as the all, analogy, matter, and being. . . . Teilhard, in point of fact, is quite familiar with these principles. But he declines to use them in the usual philosophical way, in a way, that is, which is none of his business, while still uncovering, as a professional scientist, a *new* phase, the scientific, material, and biological phase of them. It is this phase, in all its originality, of philosophical princi   which is the main object of scientific phenomenology or hyperphysics. Two errors are to be avoided when, for instance, Teilhard uses the idea of analogy: to think that he does so strictly in the context of the homology of classical biology without any philosophical reference at all, and thus that he is wrong when he homologizes beings of different natures; and to think that he is unconsciously operating within the frame of philosophical analogy, and accordingly that he has only an incomplete view of it, so that he is led to see continuity where there is only discontinuity. In reality, Teilhard develops an entirely new view, the *real nature of biological analogy,* which is actually the *biological view* of philosophical analogy. It is the same analogy, but seen from a particular standpoint which perforce favors the escape—to repeat Daujat's apt phrase—of the real nature of *formal discontinuity,* yet favors the subsistence therein of an important aspect of material discontinuity, the leaps marking the progress of structures and organic natures. These, moreover, seen at a distance, still give an impression of continuity, especially when compared to the formal discontinuities of metaphysics. There is no call, therefore, to talk about the inadequacy of Teilhard's ideas. We need, rather, to explain the *fresh originality* of this point of view, and the fact that it *is not all-inclusive.* Teilhard never pretended that it was. It is well, in the interests of prudence, to repeat for those who have forgotten it and who pretend to be quite content with the Teilhardian viewpoint, that Teilhard never pretended that it was.

The Synthetic Mind: the Evolutionary Mind

The scientific phenomenologist, then, must have a *synthetic mind.* He must, in other words, feel the need to rise above incidental detail in order to use it for an understanding of the

33

whole. This synthetic mind, this power of abstraction, of grasp of the essential, of recognition of "the one in the many," is a fundamental characteristic of the human mind as distinguished from brute psychism. Our aptitude for metaphysics is proof of our metaphysical nature. But like any human power, it grows only with use. In past, man's bent for scientific analysis, so absorbing and exciting, has been in the search of the incidental detail, and this has tended to make almost impossible the withdrawal necessary to produce a judgment of the whole. In fact, it was formerly the role of philosophers, writers, and poets to engage in synthesis while withdrawing from common sense data in a day when science was yet rudimentary. But the development of science has been such that an educated man or a philosopher, who is often totally lacking in a scientific education,[1] is not equipped with a faculty for practical synthesis, a synthesis, that is, based on a scientific conception of the world, and this at a time when scientific and technical totalitarianism has convinced so many of the non-existence of non-scientific truths. This break becomes complete in a humanism, a philosophy, a traditional way of thinking which appears totally out of date because it is cut off from reality and thus technically impractical. Such a break is catastrophic for the future of a civilization which rejects its men of wisdom and gives itself blindly to the all-powerful technician, who behaves like the Sorcerer's Apprentice, always ready to do more than he knows how to handle, because his purely analytical knowledge, though it can lead to atomic energy and its practical uses, pushes him ever further from spiritual and moral values—

[1] Its particulars can be taught, but it cannot be made into some kind of present.

which he believes, in the very name of scientific objectivity, he must ignore. To understand man, we turn these days to science. That is all right, except that science seems to tell us nothing about man. That is, it gives us disconnected aspects of him while seeming utterly to resist any understanding of him in terms of values, of *norms,* of all distinctions between the *normal* and the *pathological.* Caught in the crowd of specialists unaware of their own strength and recklessly pursuing their blind dissection of reality—which ends in "entomological" classifications with everything belonging to the same, single frame of reference—man has disappeared and become nothing more than a pattern of behaviors and motivations in terms of biological, psychological, and social determinisms. We have moved from a disembodied spiritualism down into a dust of unrelated facts into whose over-all meaning no inquiry is ever made. The philosopher can only rebel against such lack of understanding, but he has neither the power nor the technical knowledge to put things right.

The divided world of science needs to be renovated. It must come to see that science is not mere research among facts for the sake of practical efficiency, but is, rather, an effort of the understanding toward *wisely* directed action. There is need of a synthesis of the sciences over and above the individual branches of science, a synthesis which will give us knowledge about ourselves and our place in the universe. Yet this necessary synthesis must not issue in a new scientific totalitarianism in which scientific definition of reality would appear the more self-sufficient in proportion to its greater insight and consistency. A synthesis of the sciences will fulfill its humanistic role only if it converges on our traditional philosophy and humanism and confirms them with all the evidence it can bring to bear. So, if it is true that synthesis is a part of scientific work and comes within the reference of science, it is no less true that the philosopher must more than ever look to his role in the face of this synthesis, which, far from substituting for philosophy, necessitates, rather, a deepening of philosophical research.

A scientist cannot help but develop the synthetic mind if he is willing to go beyond petty detail and to see the over-all significance of his work. This is not so much a matter of a philosophical mind as of plain good sense. Further, it will help to steer him from the dangers of primarism and scientistic totalitarianism and give him a little *philosophical common sense,* a view, that is, of the conceptual world the lack of which makes him so obstinate toward faith. While mechanist materialism has never been so out of date, yet never has its spirit, in its view of the world as one vast machine, been so aggressive. The division between matter and spirit is obvious in the materialist, who, though he may not minimize spirit and consciousness like the Marxists, for whom these things are simply a reflection of society, makes of them a brain-product, a real, distinct "thing." It is obvious in the spiritualist, more than ever heir to Plato and Descartes and their unrealist idealism. It is obvious in the physicist, who discovers nothing spiritual in inanimate matter, and fashions for himself a dualist conception of living matter as something animated by an external psychological principle. It is obvious, too, in the psycho-sociologist, who, though he specializes in the study of the human mind and its activity, yet declines to become interested in animal psychology and sociology. To *distinguish* various orders is good. But these people are not satisfied to distinguish—they *separate,* they put up barriers.

Each science is thus shut up in itself. The specialist in sub-atomic particles is indifferent to the physical and chemical laws caused by the architectural combinations of particles into atoms and molecules. Biochemistry, cellular physiology, and the psycho-physiology of unicellular life are also separated sciences, a fact which prevents the unique character of the properties of *cellular integration,* the basic element of true interiority, from becoming evident. The physiologist and the medical man isolate themselves in the study of one organ without seeing that this organ is a jointly responsible part of an organism, in particular of a brain and a psychism. Thus psychosomatic medicine becomes another special field, when its disposition ought to animate every field of normal and pathological physiology.

And yet, science verifies the unity of the material composition of the universe. Everywhere we find the same matter and the same forms of energy. If some minds remain grimly obstinate to a synthesis which they characterize as metaphysical, holding that the science of man comprises and is concerned with only elementary phenomena, with what their laboratory apparatus registers, though it be a phenomenon far removed from the concept of the total phenomenon of Teilhard; if some even despair of the possibility of a synthesis when faced with the jungle of detail in the various sciences, and, like Oppenheimer, orient their science in the direction of the most unrealist Hindu metaphysics, there are, nevertheless, even in the milieux of mathematics and physics, minds open to synthesis. *Cybernetics,* especially, contributes here, not so much in its comparative studies of machines and the brain, as in its mathematical theory of *information* following from the field of telecommunications. This is an operation on the most grandiose lines, since it involves the measurement of every aspect of order, and thus assumes cosmic proportions when one thinks of it in terms of negative entropy.

Yet, it is clearly the biologist, as we have seen, who, by the very nature of his work, is compelled to be concerned with synthesis. If he is accustomed to reënvision phenomena in the harmonious context of being; if he tries to explain by the physiology of integration the personal character of a composite being which cannot be precisely defined since it is the result of the functioning of an ensemble in which certain organs play a preponderant role, he then becomes quick to grasp that ensemble. In this field, he has a more practiced eye than the physicist, so much so that he is able to grasp the within of things, even of the inanimate, where the within is rudimentary. For the physicist, mind and philosophy are far-off things. But the biologist, who is familiar with the brain, the organ of mind, is forced, if he does not want to remain incomplete and superficial, to tender questions that border on philosophy. But he resolves them, as a biologist should, by pursuing that aspect of reality on which it is his mission to throw light.

But the biologist's synthetic mind does not make simply for a total vision of the creature. It goes beyond the individual in the very fact that the biologist seeks out the creature's specific characteristics. For a long time, one of the qualities attributed to science was a concern solely with the general. But the fact of the matter is that biology, if it can define species, can also determine individual characteristics in the same species, which are open to equally objective study. But the synthetic mind of the biologist *compares* these species. The comparative mind natural in biological study catalogues the different living beings. And it is not to philosophize to say that this comparative study necessarily converges on a classification of *values,* on the *objective* fact of the existence of more and less complex creatures.

Among all the organs, there is one the complexification of which has a special value. It consists of the higher nerve centers responsible for behavior, the psychism and the intelligence, the development of which determines the creature's level. It is often said, with some humor, that there is a certain childish anthropomorphism in speaking of man as the most perfect of living creatures—after all, other creatures have more agile members or more remarkable teeth. But this sort of whimsy does not face facts. What counts—and this is true of each and every organ—is the degree of development of the brain, and here the prerogative of man is indisputable. This is not a philosophical position. It is scientific certitude. One can indeed see objectively how man resembles and how he differs from the brute. Where the psychologist, who must draw his conclusions from external behavior, is often without any clear standard of comparison between brute and man, the biologist, on the basis of organic differentiation, is able to judge from all points of view—for instance, with respect to intelligence, love, communal life, and the objective development which distinguishes insect, fish, bird, mammal, and, finally, man. This necessity for comparison in order to give man his proper place is one of the most useful aspects of the synthetic mind in the field of modern biology. It is a new aspect, because for a long time no one understood the real extent of biological growth as a standard of human classification. When one tries to transplant into man the right of the strongest in the name of the struggle for survival, or to justify racism on biological grounds; when Freud, insisting that instincts must not be repressed, tends to overlook the higher aspect of human control of instinct; when Kinsey, in his classification of human sexual behavior, declines to distinguish norms or seems to ignore the fact that the normal man is capable of self-control; when Rostand, contrary to Bernard, denies freedom by positing it as part of a pattern of drives beyond the reach of any control—in face of all this, it is stretching things to say that these men speak as biologists. Philosophers and moralists remember that man is more than a biological thing. These positions are, in fact, long-standing scientific errors. They consist in a refusal to see the complete, over-all, biological dimensions of man, the specific properties of his brain. And so it is that, with this whole biological scheme in mind, we must take up, in biological terms, the arguments in defense of human values so as to substantiate them in the eyes of those who believe only in science, and to open their minds to certitude at other levels of being. For science, though it does not, as science, know these values, yet confirms their reality and discerns an aspect of them.

But the comparative mind is not the synthetic mind at its highest level. If zoölogical classification had but one actual value, it would be of little significance. Complexification has an *historical* aspect. It is an actual witness to a history. The synthetic mind of the biologist is in essence the *sense of time*—the idea, that is, that creatures not so much are as that they are in process, are becoming, not in a total relativism, but becoming that which they were in potency to be to the degree which environment and, in man's case, individual will, let them. This sense of time, which Bergson analyzed, is woefully lacking in any number of thinkers. Yet it is an essential element in understanding reality. The man who does not have it is half-blind, and a humanism which forgets this time-dimension is worthless. Such is not Judeo-Christian humanism with its sacred history, its insertion of God into history on an eschatological coördinate.

The synthetic mind first perceives this time-dimension at the level of the *history of the individual:* man is first an egg, a single cell, humbler than an amoeba, despite the specifically human living matter which proves him already to be a man. Embryology describes in detail the whole process of individual autoconstruction—organs, then behavior—while neurophysiology and child psychology show us the final development in the progressive acquirement of a human consciousness, a hereditary potentiality dependent on favorable organic and environmental, notably social, conditions. It is striking that certain conservative positions in politics are founded on a biological error[1] which greatly overemphasizes the importance of heredity as something not to be altered by social justice which could create a far more democratic humanity in terms of individual ability.

But there is another aspect of time which draws the biologist necessarily on to the highest degree of synthesis. It is the recognition of the biological evolution of species which gives man, the crowning point of the evolutionary process, a rank of cosmic importance. The evolutionary mind, which is an essential quality of the synthetic approach in biology and on which Teilhard, as

---

[1] The work, alas, of numerous biologists, geneticists in particular.

a scientist, based all his thinking, must be clearly understood, for there is great danger of confusion. Whenever evolution is mentioned, some philosophers answer that it is an unproven theory, and so, they ask, how can any argument be based on it? Others, calling themselves fixists, reject evolution as being a total relativism which is designed to make possible the origination of the complex in the simple, and this, they say, is absurd. Others offer sound criticisms of the evolutionary theories of mutation, Lamarckism, natural selection, and ask if they really suffice to account for such important transformations in species. The biological evolutionists, on the other hand, are in a good position to show that true fixism (Lavocat) is an absurdity, for the spontaneous generation of complex species, even in egg forms, in different epochs of the earth's history is inadmissible.

In reality, everyone should be an evolutionist, it being clearly understood that this implies only recognition of a history of life on earth which is characterized by the appearance of ever more complex forms. Biology assures us that the only verifiable origin of these new forms lies in their abrupt appearance by a complete structural rearrangement in the gametes of preceding creatures—not in the sense of a species which is self-transformed, but of a transformation effected in a species in virtue of the historic potentialities for progress in life amid given environmental conditions. Here is an *ontological fixism* which has due regard for the proper nature of each species. It is, withal, a *biological evolutionism of the conditions of fulfillment,* of biological mechanism, that is, peculiar to the evolutionary process. We shall never know everything about them, but they constitute simply a level of scientific interpretation which, far from excluding, on the contrary logically demand another, a philosophical, interpretation. This interpretation must and will not attempt to oppose the idea of biological evolution to the idea of a metaphysical creation realizing itself through the mechanics of evolution. When the evolutionary mind, thus crowning the synthetic mind in biology, succeeds in giving historical meaning to the animal series and to man, there remains only a last vaulting leap to see whether, in consequences of the properties of the human brain, man, contrary to the brute—since he originally has his own biological nature and organism and brain—has thereby received an organ which makes possible a boundless psycho-social progress. History thus appears as an extension of evolution which allows man to attain his full stature, to realize his entire potentiality. Without stepping outside his own province, and because he has withdrawn sufficiently to bring his subject into focus, the biologist can thus arbitrate disputes about the existence of a *meaning of history*. He can, while staying objective, "prophesy." Not that he knows precisely what coming events will be—that depends on contingency and human freedom. But he can foresee what ought to happen if evolution follows through normally on its course and carries out its promises. The evolutionary mind scientifically demonstrates the error of those who say they believe in the absurdity of a world where such a process exists.

But there are a great many biologists, even paleontologists and experts in the study of evolution, who do not share the great Teilhardian vision. Should we therefore conclude that the vision is not objective, not scientific? By no means. These scientists, although their work is within the province of evolution, are not concerned about evolution. They have no powers of ascent, of

43

focus, none to soar across the millenniums. They do not have the synthetic mind, and refuse to apply Bernard's rule of seeing the detail in relation to the whole. This by no means hinders them from being eminent experts, and they do much to forward, say, paleontological progress with their descriptions of the complexification of Ammonite wall-building or the evolution of tumors on the molars of certain species. These things, too, have to do with evolution, the multiplicity of chance variations and adaptations of detail. Indeed, such things are the very stuff of evolution. But they are seen in magnification, and while that is necessary, it does not suffice. The meaning of evolution is clear only to the man who compares values in the animal series and cerebral complexifications at various world-epochs, just as the meaning of history often escapes historians wrapped up in the ins and outs of petty historical detail.

It is remarkable that, while so many philosophers are destitute of this time-sense, the Marxists, so destitute of the true philosophic mind—which should close them off to the synthetic[1]—on the contrary surpass most sociologists in the importance they attach to the meaning of history. For them, humanity achieves a real socio-structural progress in terms of consciousness and liberation. By contrast, many a sociologist believes that it is to be scientifically objective to protest all consideration of human values in civilization and social structures. As with Kinsey and his study of sexual behavior, they are satisfied simply to describe these values and structures and to analyze their outer machinery.

[1] This would seem to indicate that the synthetic approach is not restricted to philosophy, but has a scientific aspect as well.

Marxism, while unfortunately unaware of its full significance, recognizes this truth and owes it to the influence of biology and the teachings of evolution which Marx and, especially, Engels got from Darwin, and which confer on certain of Marx's writings a close relationship with Bernard. It is this open window of Marxism on biology which gives optimistic ground for thinking that modern biology may yet inject a certain ameliorative realism into it. Some signs of this are observable in certain aspects of the neurophysiological sciences and pedagogy in the U.S.S.R. We might also point out here that Marxism is essentially a development of a scientific conception of the world which, in its philosophical inadequacy, is satisfied to account for everything in terms of the complexification of matter, while declining to study this matter otherwise than scientifically. Marxism is a scientific phenomenology of matter which, in the name of totalitarianism, proclaims itself a metaphysical materialism. We shall have to return to the great Marxist principle which says that quantitative complexification causes the appearance of new qualities. Right here is a phenomenological truth which does not at all prove materialism, that is to say, matter as a sufficient explanation of reality. In its scientific aspect, Marxist realism converges on something which Aristotle and St. Thomas took ontological account of: the existence of forms with *metaphysically different natures*. It is well to recall this connection of Marxism with scientific phenomenology, because it explains certain apparent analogies between Teilhard's thought and the Marxists' (Engel's dialectic of nature), and at the same time the really essential difference between them. And Teilhard is the very man, in speaking their language, to provide the Marxists with a way out to the true dimensions of reality. The Marxist scientific phenomenology is crippled by a metaphysical void. Teilhard's genuine scientific phenomenology reaches its full perfection in a coronation by the solid metaphysics of which it senses significant aspects.

II

The Scientific Phenomenology
of Consciousness

(Complexification and Consciousness)

WE have defined the position and the meaning of scientific phenomenology, as Teilhard conceives it to be, in accordance with the promising but little recognized trends in the contemporary movement in science. We must now quickly call to mind the great truths on which this general vision of the world throws light, and see that world as science does, with a will to study it in its entirety, yet without departing from the scientific point of view. There is no question here of re-writing *The Phenomenon of Man*. We want rather to draw forth from it certain general propositions which will show that, appearances to the contrary, strictly scientific propositions are involved, and that they are, in their way, a light which the biologist can provide scientists for a fuller understanding of man and the universe. This does not mean superseding these specialists, psychologists, historians, philosophers, or trying to do their work for them. It only means making available to them a point of view which complements human biology—the science of the

47

creature, man—and historical biology, the comparative science which reveals man's meaning by showing him to be the end result of complexification in the animal series.

Teilhard is a scientist, not because he talks superficially about every branch of science when, in fact, he has knowledge of only one—paleontology; he is only Teilhard pondering on man, as a paleontologist, as a trained expert who presses to the uttermost every possibility in the general knowledge of man which his particular science allows him. His limitation consists in a deliberate refusal to step outside his own field. This cannot be said too often. It is as paleontologist that Teilhard sees the world, and it is because he understands the meaning of the past that he can prophesy the future, thereby resembling, in a way, the biblical "prophet," that witness who, by grace, is a surety of God's will in history. Certainly, Teilhard has no intention of philosophizing. But even in his synthetic views, he speaks purely of what his study of biological evolution has revealed to him. He is so careful in this regard that he does not attempt to give a scientific explanation of such things, for instance, as the "within of things," "consciousness," (whose biological character he observes), because he is not a neurophysiologist. Hence, it is absolutely necessary that other scientific specialists work to confirm his view by showing that the within of things and consciousness are not just purely philosophical concepts forcibly introduced into evolution, but are essential qualities of the being which biology considers one aspect of. It is important to understand clearly that the synthetic mind of the trained specialist does not take him beyond the boundaries of his field, obligated though he is to take into consideration the entire ensemble of the sciences from the viewpoint of that special field. We can hardly expect the paleontologist to keep strictly to the field of the history of life and yet take no interest in the first appearances of life. For the evolutionist as such, the inanimate is "pre-life," inert matter having evolved previously to life. He must, hence, investigate in what degree life and pre-life differ and are alike in the material aspects of their essence and in the dialectic of their evolution. Likewise, how can a neurophysiologist take no interest in cell integration with the excuse that the cell has no nervous system, that a question of the uppermost level of "pre-nervous" behavior is involved? How should he confine his study to the fully developed nervous system and pay no heed to the historic aspects of how embryological construction builds this nervous system, how biological evolution has issued in the human brain? And how can these two specialists, having taken a look at the foundations, the inanimate, take no interest in the topmost level, that is, in that which makes man a spiritual and social being? How can the paleontologist leave man at the point of his first appearance and take no interest in his subsequent history? Does not prehistory move in gradual transition? Faced with Lascaux's pictures, paleontologists and students of the human mind may not part company. So far as the neurophysiologist is concerned, his essential task is to remind us that man is incarnate, and that the highest reaches of the spiritual have an aspect, an organic substructure, with which he must beware of equating the former. Nor may he ignore them on pain of misunderstanding everything in man and terribly mutilating him.

49

The Within of Things: Integration: Consciousness

Teilhard's most significant statement is that, since "in the depths of ourselves, beyond any debate, there appears, as through a rent, an interior at the heart of being," it must follow not that man is an exception and that this interiority does not concern science, but that "there is enough to warrant saying that, to one degree or another, this 'interior' is posited as existing in nature everywhere and since the beginning of time. Since, with respect to itself, the stuff of the universe has an internal face, it follows that it be *bi-faced in structure.* That is to say, in every region of space and time . . . coextensive with their without, there is a within of things."

Never has a proposition been more misunderstood. The scientists protest that the within does not concern science. The within pertains to the spiritual, the psychic, and so the physicist rejects this childish anthropomorphism which seems to imply giving an interiority, a consciousness, to the inanimate. It amounts to a return to animism. It smells of pan-psychism. It is explaining the lesser by the greater, in which man serves as the measure of everything, whereas he is but an exception in a cold, inhuman cosmos, a being in revolt against nature, a "denatured" animal which must cling to obedience to its spirit and repulse the evil temptations of its body.

But here is where Teilhard explains the within of things. He shows its scientific aspect while still explaining its origin in the context of a history. In the course of time, there appear creatures that are more and more complex, not in that they possess more and more complicated mechanisms, but in that they are more and more richly organized, more and more centered, that is, unified and integrated. This is the law of *complexity-consciousness,* a law of complexification-centralization which Grenet rightly calls Teilhard's Law.

But here arises a fresh objection from the philosophers' corner. It is not that Teilhard is to be blamed for explaining the less by the more, but the more by the less. He is accused of materialism and held to educe spirit from simple, material complexification, as does Marxism. In particular, although he is explicit enough about it, he is accused of mingling different orders of being. Taking his conception for a sort of philosophy, his adversaries say that he brings too close together, or even identifies, the brute psychism and the human mind. His thesis about the presence of consciousness at every level of being is not taken as the sane recognition of the biological aspect of analogy —neither a confusion nor a division—as a recognition of the similar in the different. He is accused of trying to confer the same consciousness on a pebble, an amoeba, a dog, on man.

Yet, Teilhard is not an animist, an "unrealist" who humanizes nature. He is a scientist objectively describing the real.

Without any philosophizing on our part, simply by means of the interconnection of the various scientific orders, what is it we see in nature, from the electron up to man, if not more and more highly organized and integrated creatures? From the scientist's point of view, what is living matter if not the same atoms and the same energy as in the inanimate world, but with an architectural pattern, an infinitely more complex macromolecular organization conferring entirely new properties? And when there is question not of living matter, but of life itself, that is, of living being where life consists in a functional use of the properties of living matter for purposes of subsistence, of self-repair, self-multiplication, or reproduction, in a hostile world, the fundamental thing is the way in which *auto-coördination* assures functional harmony, that is, gives *finality* to commonplace physiochemistry. Scientists once tried to explain cellular permeability by means of simple physiochemical models, and the attempt failed. This was not because cellular permeability is a mysterious property of life having nothing to do with ordinary physiochemistry. It was because they made their models too simple, borrowing from inanimate structures, whereas the physiochemical architecture of the cellular membrane made of organic matter is infinitely more complex. If our knowledge allowed us to reproduce this structure artificially, we would discover the laws of permeability. But it would be difficult, because, in reality, life is not a structure. It is a fluctuating structuration in a state of constant change which by auto-coördination automatically adapts its structure and needs.

The cell is thus a little world apart, with its own individuality and interiority. Everything in it takes place in a peculiar architectural pattern, everything bows to the law of the whole, to that integration which is not a special unifying force, but a way of functioning as one thing. This integration, this organic, anatomo-physiological interiority, is, in the scientific phenomenologist's view, of the same nature as mental interiority, for, like it, the latter results from organization, from dynamic structuration.

For anyone who reflects on life, the significant, enduring thing is not atoms, not matter, though certainly, without matter, there is no life. But atoms go through a process of unceasing replacement, even in the cells of the human brain. What endures unchanged is the structure and its functional capacities. It is like a wall in which the bricks are being constantly changed, yet keeping their same place, so that the wall, as wall, is always the same. Here is an objective, sure conclusion of modern biology which is not at all a philosophical one, and yet is of paramount concern to philosophers. While we keep our distance from the old materialism which sought to localize and "reify" life, and from idealist vitalism and its useless vital principle animating inert matter, we must not confound levels. In our scientific analysis as such, we remain at the level of material operations where the spiritual is revealed only in the enduring organization of this fluctuating matter. Nothing is more spiritual than its organization allows it to be. But it would be of no use to scientific analysis without the organized atoms. The scientist, while distinguishing between organization and its organized elements, is yet obliged not to separate them. The study of organization, of integration, is the primary concern of science, and science must determine its material, functional mechanism.

Teilhard gives this integration a spiritual dimension. He calls it consciousness. This is not the distortion of a believer who puts a soul into everything. That Teilhard does nothing of the sort is confirmed by Lapicque, who was a perennial materialist. Lapicque steadily refused to adopt the so-called objectivity of psychophysiologists who declined to discuss, as scientists, the soul, or the consciousness and will, of near-to-human animals, and at the end of his life and in line with his own beliefs, he was angered by the pretensions of certain non-biological specialists in cybernetics who asserted the possibility of constructing a machine complex enough to be endowed with a real consciousness analogous to ours. This was a scientific blunder due not to a materialist position, but to a mechanist deviation from materialism. To the scientist, consciousness appears phenomenologically as the consequence of a complexification process, but as an organic complexification, particularly of cerebral organization. To think that by complexifying an inanimate, electronic organization one will imitate life, is to show an utter lack of biological common sense, and to disregard degrees of being. Complex as it may be, any inanimate construct will always be infinitely simple compared to living matter, to an organism, which possesses a specific, constitutive dimension of hypercomplexity: the chemical composition of living matter and cellular organization. A machine, perfect as it may be, will always be nothing but a collection of parts organized by an external action. It will never be an auto-construction such as the organism resulting from the division of an ovum. In thinking about the profound difference which distinguishes the mechanical from the vital, Lapicque, while adhering explicitly only to scientific canons, concluded that there was question of a unified, integrated aspect of vital being which, despite its pluricellular composition, is nonetheless *one,* without this unity depending on the direct action of a separate metaphysical principle. For him, this organic integration is—in brief—the biological aspect of the soul or of *consciousness,* and he did not, contrary to so many psychobiologists, think such terms to be in contradiction of scientific objectivity. (The height of objectivity is to recognize the subjective!) If the organism is biologically endowed with consciousness, this means, for Lapicque, that it is made up of living cells, and that its total consciousness is the result of an integration of consciousness or of *cellular souls*. There is certainly no childish anthropomorphism, no departure from strict science, in recognizing that the cell functions as an integrated whole, that it is a tiny elementary individuality defending its life. Like Teilhard, but in a materialist context, Lapicque thus makes consciousness the essential property of every living thing, however simple it may be, and biological phenomenology leads him to conclude that "the soul is immaterial but not immortal." Such is the evolution which science imposed on scientific materialism, which was thus forced to confess to the specific spiritual character of the psychological aspect of organic integration. Where there had been hopes of an isolable, material, organic product, it turned out to be a question of an immaterial process resulting from the over-all functioning of the organism, particularly of the brain.

Thus we see how tendencies in scientific progress compel even the materialist to consider the material aspect of the spiritual. If some scientists still shrink, in their prejudice against metaphysics, from this notion of consciousness, their position is untenable, for no neurophysiologist today can remain indifferent to the cerebral mechanics of consciousness. While Western psychology and pedagogy are held to be more scientific because they ignore consciousness, Soviet psychopedagogy, while tenaciously materialistic, does not hesitate to insist on its importance quite as much as do the spiritualist philosophers. However, it sees it as a biological property, which is a strictly scientific conclusion. Where science overshoots the mark is to conclude that there is only this level of scientific explanation, that the human consciousness or soul is only organic integration. When Lapicque concluded to the mortality of the spiritual soul, he made it very clear that his conclusion concerned only the organic aspect of integration. His conclusion, therefore, is scientifically valid, even for the spiritualist who does not share his materialist, metaphysical faith.

Some will say that, since this consciousness, this soul, of which biologists thus speak, is not the metaphysical principle, we end in confusion by using the same words in different senses. But as a matter of fact, it is much the same reality which is perceived by the metaphysician and the biologist, each taking, however, his own proper point of view. The cause of any confusion, quite to the contrary, is the failure to understand that it is a question of a single reality, and then making out of it two unrelated concepts.

The Degrees of Consciousness

To give a within, an interiority, and consciousness to all living creatures, as Teilhard does, is thus only to voice a tendency in all the contemporary psychobiological sciences. The fact is incontestable, even if the terminology is sometimes objectionable. No one any longer agrees with Loeb that the behavior of the lower orders of creatures can be reduced to the simple automatism of tropisms. Involved as they are with the sense-perception of living matter, tropisms are certainly an element in behavior. But they are integrated with any unified, finalized behavior-complex, if it is a true, inferior psychism, where Viaud finds, in germ form, everything that exists in creatures of a higher order. The level of the unicellular is not passively acted on by its environment. It actively reacts by adaptation. Comparative—or objectivist—psychology, which has completed precise scientific analysis of instinctive behavior, has here had to turn its thoughts to the level of animal psychology and has thus determined that the latter was not only an affair of elementary behavior patterns, but also of an integration of these patterns. Its objectivity ended in an animal subjectivity which it is impossible to deny.

There is question here of clearly understanding just what this animal consciousness is. There is no question at all of returning to the errors of the old anthropomorphism which attributed to animals our thoughts, our feelings, our will. Scientific psychology has clearly shown that animals have nothing of the sort, and has objectively discredited the elementary automatisms of conduct. But it went too far in denying certain complex data which, though clearly observed, were but poorly explained by the old naturalists. Scientific progress today makes it possible for us to rediscover these data and give them a realist interpretation. As for the animal-machine, any caricature of man, there is no such thing. There are differing degrees in the animal psychism. These degrees are determined not only by the complexity of the behavior under analysis, but especially by the degree of integration, of control, of interiority, of consciousness.

Thus, when the philosopher rebels against this extension of consciousness, it is because he has not understood that the biologist, by the nature of his work as a specialist in biological organization, finds it impossible to confuse the various levels of consciousness, which depend on the degree of organic and, especially, nervous complexity.

The biologist does not, in complete confusion born of a false analogy, liken the higher to the lower or the lower to the higher. Rather, he recognizes objectively the *real analogy* of creatures in its *biological aspect,* while estimating the psychological possibilities of their degree of organization. People are always trying to express everything in terms of continuity or discontinuity. Thus, either man is alone in having consciousness, or the human consciousness has the same nature as animal consciousness. From the viewpoint of comparative neurophysiology, each of these propositions is false. Human consciousness both resembles and is different from brute consciousness at the same time. The relationship is very deep, since in both instances it is dependent on biological and especially nervous integration. But just so: The advance of organic and nervous integration is such, in man, that even from the biological point of view, a great step has been taken. There is discontinuity in the continuity, a real difference in biological nature. This implies no metaphysical conclusion on the biologist's part, but it does require that the philosopher be asked for an opinion.

The remarkable advances of the neurophysiology of the human brain, be it in the Pavlovian context of the conditioned reflexes of language, or in the development of the neurosurgical study of the brain in its waking state, today give its full dimension to *human biology.* Biology is no longer the science of what in man more or less resembles the brute—matter, the organic, the body, as opposed to soul. Thanks to neurophysiology, it is the science of the organic aspect of the top reaches of the specific

58

spiritual character of man, for it is not a spiritual function which necessitates a mechanism, a cerebral substructure. These mechanisms are not a sort of elementary system of wheels at the service of a separate thought-process which activates them. Whatever be the process of its emergence, or its transcendence, this thought-process is immerged among the wheels which it activates from within. It is immanent in them, which is the reason why the scientific aspect cannot separate the spiritual from the cerebral mechanism, and why human cerebral mechanisms have a complexity proportioned to the highest human spirituality. It is thus an utterly traditional apologetic, aimed at proving the immortality of the soul from the peculiarities of the human mind in comparison with the brute psychism, that becomes less valid. For if the materialist formerly minimized the mind of man in his very phenomenology, this is no longer so. Marxism, since Engels and even more since Pavlov, considers the superior value of the human mind a consequence of the superiority of the brain which gives it birth. There is need, then, to re-think the traditional arguments by showing the necessity of a metaphysical explanation of human cerebral superiority, which is, in fact, superiority of soul. Spiritualist philosophers and biologists should not deny human cerebral superiority and the compelling explanation it affords of the material organic aspect of all spirituality. They should aim at making clear that what is involved is the immanent aspect of a soul, whose full dimension is transcendent and is the very thing which accounts for the superiority of biological integration and its cerebral powers of logic, science, and metaphysics.

We are betrayed by a language which is but poorly made for

the expression of analogies. Prehuman consciousness is practically in no respect similar to human consciousness, since the latter is a word-using reflection-process situate wholly above action and allowing for normal advance toward true freedom of control and judgment. The brute, by reason of its cerebral deficiency, cannot have this degree of consciousness or this freedom. In an inferior degree, nonetheless, it does show awareness of action and control, a capacity for elementary judgment, a utilization of experience, a prehuman level of intelligence. All psychologists today agree in speaking of *animal intelligence,* and in seeing in it the germ of something that in man will reach full development. The brute is not wholly a thing of the automatisms of instinct and training. It possesses, in a degree proportionate to the development of its higher nervous centers, the possibility of controlling them in terms of a better comprehension of situation and of command of a better adapted activity, indicating control of experience and the fact that it has in its head distinct memories which it can utilize. It is impossible these days to separate the brute psychism from the human psychism by a strict line of division. Granted, no one would dream of making the mistake of identifying them or of denying that in man this psychism takes on new dimensions. Everything in the traditional view about the peculiar features of the human mind, which give to human intelligence its own special character, remains true, but a recognition of the specific character of its peak development in no way requires a denial of the continuity of the steps which lead up to it, even if this argues for an especially momentous leap from brute to man.

It is impossible to restrict intelligence to man. Yet there must be objective distinctions between the animal level of intelligence and the human which alone is conceptual and metaphysical, though this in no way forbids it to express itself by means of specific cerebral mechanism. In the same way, we must also admit *animal consciousness,* and describe the picture of organic and nervous gradations in the animal series as advances in integration resulting in advances in consciousness. This does not prevent us from giving a unique place apart to the jewel of this complexification, the human consciousness. This same difference of level exists, moreover, in the area of the unconscious. There is an animal unconsciousness, but, like its consciousness, it, too, is rudimentary. They are only less distinct and their psychological import weak. Something especially characteristic of man here is the great psychic content of his unconscious.[1] This involves the greater part of cerebral functions, though it is sharply separated from the conscious. It is especially evident in neuroses —the pathological lot of human superiority—and found but rarely in the brute, and then, usually, only in experimentally induced conflicts and to a much less complex degree.

Bioconsciousness and Zoöconsciousness

This analogy describes from top to bottom of the scale of life a nature common to the interior psychological aspect of integration, a nature comprised of levels so diverse that one can in some degree speak of psychological natures which are different for

[1] This includes not only the depths of the Freudian unconscious, but also the summits of the *transconscious* from which come metaphysical and mystical intuitions.

different kinds of consciousness. To express this analogy, we propose special prefixes to be added to the word "consciousness." From its beginning, cellular life has interiority and consciousness which possess, in the self-control of physiological and psychophysiological cellular behavior, an undeniable psychic aspect. It is impossible to introduce between the inanimate and the animal psychic state a purely biological stage minus a psychism. All life is a psychism because it is motivated, adaptive behavior responding to internal needs whose material, physiochemical side should not make us forget the more hidden psychological aspect. The two aspects of interiority are complementary and inseparable. Integrated material interiority is at the root of psychological interiority.

The obvious distinction between them in man, though spiritual interiority here always depends on cerebral conditions, should not blind us to the much more restricted relationship of the two aspects in the lower orders of life. Thus, we have chosen the name "bioconsciousness" for this elementary consciousness of living cellular matter. It is a consciousness which results from a non-nervous integration based on physiochemical cellular individuality, that is, on the fact that the cell is a harmonious whole which makes its own way in the world. The study of this bioconsciousness, though it is an important chapter requiring study and special experimentation in the physiology of cell integration, need not turn to metaphysics.

It is important, further, to point out that this bioconsciousness is proper to every cell. This is the more true in cells of the higher organisms, which have it in a more developed state in proportion to their enjoyment of more complex and independent behavior (highly autonomous behavior such as that of the spermatozoon or nerve fiber in process of growth). It is a special problem, as much for the physiology of the individual as for the philosophy of it, for example the spermatazoon capable of independent life in separation from its parent individual. This human bioconsciousness in a particular cell which, in all the details of its operation, possesses nonetheless the complete structure of the species and the individual, will be found again in the higher pluricellular creature when growth begins. At the start, every creature is a single cell, an *egg,* whose degree of consciousness may be less than that of an amoeba. This is the case of the human egg, a parasite in the mother and almost wholly void of behavior. And yet, the entire future individual is there in a potential state, made of specifically human living matter and ready to supply a brain with its proper hereditary characteristics. The bioconsciousness of the human egg, inferior to the bioconsciousness of the free amoeba, is a human bioconsciousness. It is an incarnate condition of the human soul which, as the principle of the reflective adult consciousness, has consequently a common dimension with that consciousness.

This bioconsciousness is not peculiar to the cell alone, whether it be the bioconsciousness of the whole individual, unicellular or egg, or a bioconsciousness normally subordinated to a higher consciousness, as in the case of the cells of a complex organism. Whether they have no true nervous centers or they be but rudimentary—like the nerve cords of the echinoderm and lower worm, the cerebroid ganglia of the worm or of higher invertebrates little blessed in this respect—all lower pluricellular creatures remain at this rudimentary level of elementary bioconsciousness. The entire creature, the whole integration of cellular bioconsciousness, stands at a level not much higher than the cells of which it is constituted.

When, on the other hand, we meet creatures provided with higher centers such as the cerebroid ganglia assuring a true psychism, say, in the insect, especially the social insect, or the spider, the crustacean, the mollusk, the cephalopod such as the octopus or cuttlefish; or centers such as the elementary brain, minus a cortex, in the lower vertebrate (the fish, the frog) bioconsciousness becomes more highly psychological and assures much richer, more adaptive behavior. Here, indeed, is the first degree of thought and animal consciousness, but a thought and consciousness far removed from ours, and which is almost completely plunged in the automatisms of instinct and conditioned reflexes. Very rare are the situation-judgments which allow the insect to repair the mistakes it makes under experimental provocation. Here it is all a matter of *instinctive zoöconsciousness*. We must emphasize the fact that such a zoöconsciousness has nothing to do with the pseudo-consciousness peculiar to instinct, which is a mysterious metaphysical force it was once customary to oppose to intelligence. Instinct is an elementary degree of brute intelligence, sometimes more marked in certain individuals. But there is no specific consciousness in it. Instinct today is reducible to a chain of elementary behavior-reflexes, properties of a type of peculiar organic structure. The possibility of innate reactions, as of the acquired reactions of training, is a part of the elementary biological mechanisms, and these reactions are therefore at the level of bioconsciousness, where they are part of an automatic integration unknown to the true rudimentary consciousness of the brute.

To find a condition of consciousness really related to ours, we must go to creatures possessed like ourselves of a cerebral cortex, especially the bird and the mammal. Their *higher zoöconsciousness* gives them a far greater control of the automatisms of behavior, awareness of action, utilization of experience and judgment in the correction of mistakes, power recognizing a neighbor as such and of having with it a true social relation of friendship and love. As Lapicque observed, it is impossible, at this level, not to talk about thought, will, feeling, provided we do not wholly identify these powers with our own. A stronger proof of this relationship of consciousness is that, at this level, an interpsychological relation is possible with man, the relation of *domestication,* which is not possible at a lower level. Owners of dogs, cats, or birds are wrong to think that an animal is of their own level, to think, for instance, that an animal understands their language in a human way. But they are right to insist on the possibility of psychological communication. This is found at the level of animal consciousness when carried to the educative limit of domestication. The parrot uses words and phrases and imitates them wittingly in a given situation, but it uses human speech as a learned system of animal signal-sounds and in no way creates the interior conceptual language, the way of thinking, peculiar to the human brain alone. Instead of thus elevating the animal, one can also pretend to assume a place at its own level. This is what modern zoöpsychologists do, such as Lorentz when he makes himself a jackdaw among jackdaws or plays father goose to young goslings. This would be impossible at the level of lower animals, a level at which man can use the animal but without any psychological rapport, as in the case of bees. One can understand a dog, but one cannot understand a snake. A snake charmer knows only the sensory stimuli which cause the snake to act, and thus he can handle it without danger.

Human Consciousness and Cultural Progress

Reflective consciousness appears only when we reach the human level. This new area of consciousness is closely related to the cerebral progress, which allows for greater integration, and for a more complete self-awareness of the subject. The image of the body in the brute brain remains rudimentary and immanent in action. But because of the potentialities of the human brain, its complexification gives it an individual character such that it can become the *subject* of feelings and actions. This is a capacity peculiar to man which has existed from the beginning, and which differentiates the biological nature of the anthropoid with a less developed brain from that of man. Because of a cerebral lack, the anthropoid is incapable of thought and human consciousness, a fact which is especially in evidence by the absence of a *real language*.

However, in the dialectical picture of the intimate relation between consciousness and organic complexification, there appears a new element peculiar to man, one which is to be defined not merely in terms of the possession of consciousness of another order in relation to his more complex brain. Whereas, in the animal, training and education alter consciousness only to a slight degree, in man education is necessary to give reflective consciousness its full dimension if it is to differ significantly from the higher level of animal consciousness. The brain in itself is not enough. It furnishes only an elementary potentiality which will develop only if one makes a human use of it. The human psychological use of the brain depends on the acquisition of a *cultural language* rooted in a social environment. In the case of animals, community life, despite the significant modifications it introduces in their customs, is not a source of a real growth. In man's case, it is quite otherwise. Man is naturally social and possesses a brain suitable to *progress*. Instead of remaining fixed at the feeble level of animal language, his brain physiology allows him not only the potentialities of richer vocalization, innate or acquired, but particularly that of transforming this communication code into a means of thought. Man replaces *thinking in images* with *verbal thinking,* which is far more apt for expressing abstractions. The language of mathematics is also a variety of cerebral structuration peculiar to man. Primitive man, because he had a brain, was capable of speech,[1] but he had no cultural language, and his verbal signals, as in the animal, served only for communication, and not for thought. It required a long process of collective evolution for the creation of a language making possible the achievment of an intellectual state. But this language is not merely a means for a purer kind of thought. It is also a means for the perfecting of consciousness, for the realization of the full power of reflection. For if the power of reflecting is an aptitude of the human brain, this aptitude remains barely realized so long as a language equipped with a grammar has not contributed toward

[1] It is not known at what human or prehuman stage this capacity became better developed than in the brute.

the *verbalization of the image of the "me"*—so long, in other words, as the subject cannot call itself "I" or "me" and thus assume the control of its thought. It is this verbalization which brings about the emergence of the "me" immanent in control, and which, stated briefly, creates a *consciousness of consciousness*. To know the evolution of languages from their very beginnings would be invaluable for understanding man. Unfortunately, these origins are lost. Present-day primitives, though we do not know in what degree they are primitive or simply regressive, are in every way highly evolved compared to their original condition. Still, we can avail ourselves of the evolution of languages, the most primitive being, psychologically, the most deficient. Human progress is especially a progress of language, and science is above all a new language. The least educated men of today are even so much nearer to the scholarly élite than the true primitives of bygone times, for the latter's feeble language allowed less for verbalization of the "me."

The physiology of consciousness—a science of the future still in its infancy—would have much to learn from the observation of men destitute of a language—children living *in a condition of isolation,* either deliberately induced or because they have been reared in an animal society (wolf-children), or because the deafness cutting them off from others has prevented the grafting of a social language on their inborn capacity for vocalizing (deaf mutes). A psychological study of these children in comparison with normal children or animals would be very fruitful for determining how much depends on the brain and how much depends on the cultural use of the brain. Unfortunately, such observation is hampered by the impossibility of experimentation and by difficulties in interpreting the tests for the verbalizing intelligence. This is the more so when the desocialized child is abnormal. Its complete isolation leads to a stoppage of cerebral functions and thus to idiocy. There are difficulties, too, when a deaf child living in normal society remains always in some sort of contact with it, even in the absence of a real language, though it may invent a means of communication, or its other senses furnish it some sort of education. The deaf mute reëducated by a sign language invented by those who do speak really possesses a cultural language, a means of thought with only minor deficiencies. In the same way, the sufferer from aphasia, who once could speak, is not utterly without a language. If he has lost the power of mentally evoking words and of pronouncing them, he still keeps the unconscious verbal automatisms which help him to think in a human way. Apart from such rare cases of a wolf-child or a deaf mute abandoned to itself, there is no possibility for studying non-verbaled human consciousness in order to evaluate its defectiveness. Moreover, the frequent objections of psychologists to the study of consciousness—stemming from a false sense of objectivity—has caused serious neglect of this important question. It has been pointed out that, in the growth of the child, it is the appearance of language and especially of the word "I" which has the effect of giving it that completely human consciousness which makes possible so many astounding advances in total development when compared to the baby monkey. Still, these advances exist also, with some deficiencies, as Olèron has shown, in the absence of language. Of prime importance here is the factor of maturation of the brain, which renders language normally possible, assuming the social milieu is not deficient.

Thus, we always find two factors in human consciousness: the largest of all brains as its origin, and the linguistic training which gives it its full dimension.

The "Heart" as Apex of Consciousness

It would be a great mistake of a narrow, rationalist sort to limit the superiority of human consciousness to its verbalization aspect. Study of the human brain shows us that, though the complexification of the *noetic* brain (the lateral and posterior brain) affords the use of an inner language to human reason and a conscious grasp of the "me," the most striking area of the brain is not here. Passing from the ordinary mammal to the primate, from the lower order of monkeys to the anthropoids, and from these to man, we find not only a complexification of the entire brain through an increase of the neurones—of the network, that is to say, of their interconnections, but also an ever greater development of one special area of the brain, the *prefrontal area*. We have learned from neurophysiology that this area is the zone of highest integration in the individual. It gives to the self its full dimension. It unites and coördinates the primitive brain of the instincts and affections with the noetic brain of language and reflection to confer power of judgment and observation concerning what must be done to achieve purpose. We might call this power "super-consciousness," or "super-reflection." This is expressed in the traditional words "heart" or "love" in their best sense, not as elementary sentimentality or the irrational, but as something transcending reason without being contrary to it, as Siewerth[1] has shown. Now this dimension, symbolized by the

[1] *L'homme et sons corps,* Paris, 1957.

human forehead as the sign of control, exists from the time of primitive man. Far from being simply a savage bordering on the animal because of defects of language which limited his reasoning and reflective powers, the primitive had an intuitive knowledge of the good, the beautiful, and the true which is sometimes wanting in the verbalizing rationalist who abandons it to atrophy and neglect. Speaking figuratively, we might say that the difference between Adam, the perfect man of tradition, and Adam, the savage of science, is only apparent. Be that as it may in view of original sin[1] (we shall return to this problem), an uneducated Adam, almost languageless and therefore with limited reflective power, was nonetheless not a perfected monkey, but a man not only equipped with the innate capacities of his brain, but also with the functions of prefrontal integration—a man with heart and love thereby readied for mystical and aesthetic knowledge, even though he was unable to express it in an abstract, verbalized, theological system, or by a technical knowledge of instrumental music.[2]

Integration Levels in the Higher Organism

As we have seen, this summit of human consciousness is the result of the embryological growth of a bioconsciousness which started from a cellular, brainless level. The ascent of conscious-

[1] The effects of original sin, it appears, do not involve the educational process so much as judgment and control, prefrontal operations that have functioned in man since the very beginning.

[2] From this point of view, painting comes more readily to the primitive in the expression of his aesthetic feelings than poetry or music. The savages of the Orinoco cannot play Mozart or create like him, but they understand and are attracted to him.

ness through complexification of the mechanisms of organic integration in the individual auto-construction continues at the human level in the improvement of the use of the brain, in cultural and social operations. It spells the acquirement of an individual, personal consciousness emerging from the collective thought of the primitive. Pre-logical as it is, it is nevertheless already human and results, in our own time, in the conflict of a rationalist egotism and social totalitarianism which denies the individual. This conflict must be resolved in a synthesis, in the personalist society of the *noösphere*. This will be a truly human community on the higher prefrontal level of consciousness.

We cannot liken embryological evolution in any strict way to the various stages which we see in the animal series. No more so can we liken the complete brute to a superior creature which has been experimentally deprived of the highest nervous centers responsible for the nobler dimensions of its consciousness. However, if the adult consciousness is the result of an ascent of consciousness parallel to the advance of nervous integration in growth, it will appear then, also, under a *hierarchical* aspect. The integration of elementary cellular bioconsciousness in the unity of the individual is achieved at ascending levels of consciousness. At the lower level of the integration of the physiological mechanisms which assure functional unity through coördination of the hormone and nerve processes making for steady operation of the body's interior—"body wisdom," as Cannon calls it—we stand at a level bordering the biological level of bioconsciousness. This automatic bioconsciousness, though we cannot localize it, nevertheless has a coördinating center in certain nuclei at the base of the brain, the *hypothalamus*. It would be a great philosophical mistake to try to localize therein the "me," the person, or to situate, as Descartes did in a sort of epiphysis, the center of action of a separate soul. But in any case, the fact remains that there is question of a true center in the integration scheme of unconscious automatisms. This center does not simply coördinate internal functions. It also controls the instinctive automatisms of life in relation to self-preservation and reproduction. It is the seat of nerve stimulus for which the self-consciousness in the brain sounds the call. It is also responsible for affective automatisms whenever the pleasurable or disagreeable or unexpected appears. It is one of the most important achievements of modern neuro-physiology to have shown that nerve control of instinct and affectivity is not in the brain itself, that desire and affectivity, which owe their conscious phase to the brain, are more than anything else unconscious nerve processes. That is, they are situate at the level of that well-ordered organization which we have called bioconsciousness. It is remarkable that, to meet the alimentary needs of our cells, there are neighboring centers controlling in succession the internal auto-regulatory process which supplies nourishment from the body's reserves. These "centers" can be purely physiological—behavior patterns of the hunt for and pursuit of food and and the alimentation which supplements any lack in the reserves, or more psychological; in any case, they are still automatic reactions. Here again, we find something which exists for the sake of cell behavior: internal coördination of cell physiology and life in relation to the environment, simple absorption of substances from without, or the elemental quest for this nourishment. It is the same with respect to sex life, where the same nearby centers control purely genital physiology and sexual behavior, which is highly complex in the animal, as the custom of courtship illustrates. This same center of bioconsciousness in higher creatures is involved, moreover, in the possibility of higher cerebral forms of consciousness, for situate there are the regulatory mechanisms of waking and sleeping and of attention, and therefore of something which makes it possible for the cerebral cortex to render us conscious.

In the lower vertebrates, which have no cerebral cortex, it is at the level of this center that the whole animal psychism and its instinctive zoöconsciousness are situate, with very weak control of innate and acquired automatisms and a minimum possibility of will. In the higher vertebrates having a cortex, the psychism is transferred there in the same way as the higher level of integration, the higher zoöconsciousness, which is close neighbor to human consciousness. Here we must further distinguish between levels of complexification. Birds have only a rudimentary cerebral cortex; their psychism and consciousness depend in particular on the important growth of a nucleus called the "hyperstriatum." The lower mammals, even the dog or the cat, when deprived of their cortex, yet remain capable of automatic instinctive activity directed toward the pleasurable and the useful and resistant to the disagreeable. Their behavior implies the existence of elementary sensation much less complex than that of cortical consciousness. In its mutilated state, the creature is reduced to the level of elementary zoöconsciousness, though in comparison to a normal lower vertebrate it keeps a higher behavior level because of the far greater complexity of its lower centers even while evidencing certain deficiencies, for its lower centers do not have all the psychic powers of complete individual integration which they have in the lower animal. On the other hand, in the primates and in man, although they are important coördinators in the normal subject, these centers become incapable of performing their duties in the absence of a cortex. Sensation in particular, which dictates behavior, depends entirely on the cortex and on a higher degree of awareness.

The Nature of Complexification

These few considerations, though we have been unable to go into them minutely,[1] should be quite enough to show that scientific, objective study of living being by the biologist, who tries to understand this being in all the manifestations of its physiology and behavior, is compelled to leave off analysis in order to elucidate the integration-mechanisms which make the creature a unified individual. To study organic integration, to see how it is realized through biological mechanisms and functions, is no part of the philosopher's work. However, the biologist is required to show that organic integration always has psychological consequences, for the degree of integration does not determine merely the degree of the complexity of behavior, but also the degree of consciousness, that is, of the individualization and personalization of conduct. This does not mean, as the old mechanist materialists thought, that consciousness is a material product of

[1] We must emphasize the whole psychological complexity and integration of the human "unconscious," that most important part of cerebral function which psychoanalysis investigates, and which is more highly organized than brute consciousness. It is especially the "consciousness" of the dream state.

the brain or of organic integration. It only means that in the unity of the creature, it has *organic conditions*. The degree of consciousness, far from being evident only to the eye of the philosopher, has an objective, scientific aspect which pertains to scientific study, and which makes up that introspective, scientific phenomenology of which it is the specific object. *All creatures have a degree of consciousness which can be evaluated by the degree of their integration.*

It is, therefore, scientifically impossible either to identify man with the brute or absolutely to separate them. Man is not a spiritual consciousness acting on a brain bordering the brute brain. From its organic and cerebral design, we see a specific complexification which reveals the organic conditions of human spirituality. This objective proposition of science must not be misconstrued by shifting it to the realm of philosophy. The fact that the human brain affords greater consciousness in no way implies either that this consciousness is of an order other than that of the brute, or that it should be identified closely with that complexity. Whether the human soul exists or not, of itself, outside the cerebral conditions which furnish evidence of it in this world, is no business of biology.

Objective study of the parallelism between the ascent of biological integration and the ascent of consciousness in the animal series up to and including man aims neither at explaining the less by the more, the amoeba by the man, nor the more by the less, man by the amoeba, but rather at assigning each creature *its biological place*. It is not a question of pan-psychism or of materialism, but of science. If, by scientific definition, man is seen as endowed with a reflective consciousness, while the amoeba has but minimal cell integration, this is not, so far as the scientist is concerned, because they have different metaphysical natures (the scientist, as scientist, is not competent here), but because man, in all his complexity, has been able to construct, on the foundation of his cell integration, a cerebral superintegration. It is this material complexification which is responsible for the development of his consciousness. Science objectively proves it, and philosophy must accept it—and explain it. It is important to grasp clearly the extent of the complexification of integration. It is not like a wall with decorations added to it, or a liver acquiring more and more cells. This sort of complication has no deep ontological meaning relative to the level of the creature. It is quite otherwise with the progress of integration. When the development of nerve centers confers on the annelide certain cerebroid ganglia as sense receptors and directors of behavior, the animal takes on a subjectivity—that is, an individuality far superior to that of a sponge or a hydra, neither of which has this central system and whose cells are more independent. The constancy of the internal conditions, and more particularly of temperature in the higher vertebrates, gives much greater individuality, and in particular affords the psychism and the brain much greater protection from external contingencies. In the anthropoid and man, the complication consists in a quadrupling of the number of cerebral neurones. If we ask why this complexification bestows being infinitely richer in psychism and consciousness, the answer is that an increase of neurones acts not quantitatively, but qualitatively. The important thing is not the number but the possibility of interconnections, which increases in an immeasurably greater degree. In man, there are some fourteen billion such interconnections. Comparison with adding machines has accustomed us to think that the possibilities increase with the complexity of the circuits, but this, as we have just seen, does not mean that a machine made of billions of parts would have a human consciousness. Unconscious parts cannot result in conscious integration. Cerebral complexification should not be taken under its analytical aspect alone, of more and more substitutional possibilities, but also under its synthetic aspect, the richer possibilities of over-all integration, of synthesis.

The objection is often made that severe brain injuries, if they spare indispensable areas, leave the psychism and consciousness untouched, and one thinks of Pasteur going on with his discoveries after his hemiplegia. At the time, he had fewer active neurones than a monkey. But the objection is invalid, because what matters is not the absolute number of neurones, but the density of their interconnections. At the moment when any area essential for perception and action cannot be directly reached, there is the possibility of substitutions by indirect routes. Cerebral connections are not made up of single, linear paths, but of multiple paths in an *interconnecting network*. Some area of the brain is always left to the complex human structure. On the other hand, the brain abounds in neurones, which make for education and cultural progress. But the important thing is the way in which the brain is used. Once the automatisms are formed, they continue to survive even after injury if it is not too great.

Thus, consciousness is not to be taken in its strictly philosophical meaning. It is a property of life, and the advance of consciousness which ends in reflective human consciousness depends organically on the growth of an organ which can perfect consciousness. It will be for the psychologist and the philosopher to decide whether there is a metaphysical difference, a formal discontinuity, between the brute, in whom consciousness is simply organic integration, and man, in whom this organic integration is an incarnation of true transcendence.

Animal Creativeness and Human Creativeness

Another aspect of the relationship of consciousness to life and man is seen in the frequently used analogy between organ and tool. The human creates the tool for an intelligent purpose. This tool, an appanage of *homo faber,* is nothing, originally, but a cerebral schema, a proof of the intelligence and wisdom of the so-called *faber.* Both the intellectual and the manual laborer use the brain. The tool is born of a cerebral structuration. Therefore, like the organ, it has a biological aspect. One wonders how nature was able to prepare a faculty of invention which creates functional forms that the creative genius of man will discover independently. But this is to put the question poorly. If man has a creative faculty, it is because he is a living being. All life is creative. The creative power of life belongs to the order of bioconsciousness, but at a lower level where it is not a matter of the individual, but of the power which living matter reveals in self-transformation while inventing new forms, structures, and organs in an interacting process between organism and environment. The most impressive example of this is the progressive complexification of the brain. This cerebral complexification ends in a personalization of the creative power of life. That which life unconsciously achieves, man consciously achieves, because he is a supercerebralized living thing. There exist as well intermediate stages in animal use of the tool, such as the wasp which closes up the hole into its nest with a pebble.

The Organization of the Inanimate and Consciousness

Once the biologist has traced out a progressive phenomenology of consciousness and interiority subject to the material conditions of their fulfillment, something which the philosopher saw as strictly spiritual now appears in its material aspect. It is a matter of integration and therefore of organization. Cell consciousness is largely material and organic. It is not at all a sort of miniature human consciousness, but the consciousness of non-nervous integration. In conditions such as these, and with the disappearance of Descartes' airtight partition between pure spirit and the animal-machine, is it possible to preserve the other partition, the separation between the living and the non-living? Is Teilhard an animist when he confers a "within" on what he calls "pre-life"? We shall see that, contrary to what the physicists and the philosophers say, we are dealing here with a scientific conclusion which results merely in an extension of the idea of integration and organization to the inanimate. No one denies that it belongs to science to explain the structure of matter as an architecture of electrons, protons, and other atomic particles, and the architecture of the atoms in the molecules. The nucleus of the atom or the molecule has an organization. We represent it in rather anthropomorphic diagrams, and stand by our mathematical expression of it. This organization is an elementary integration and gives matter its properties. While we call this matter inanimate, we now know it to be enormously animated, though of less complexity than the animation of life. If cell integration possesses the proportions of consciousness, it canniot be otherwise with the organization of the inanimate. However, the analogy here is more remote, the psychic aspect weaker than in the cell, the behavior more restricted. Such interiority is no more than an interior, a process of energized, unifying interactions. The difference holds down to the degree of least complexity in the elements. Atom, cell, or man, the various degrees of integration entail differing properties of consciousness. The organization of the inanimate is a within which has the dimension of a *pre-conscious.* Let the constituents become more complex, and consciousness arises.

In this view of the inanimate, the biologist is not guilty of the blunder of seeing the greater in the smaller, or of putting soul or mind into everything. He respects the order of being, but, trained to grapple with the integration of the whole, he is better equipped to see the root principles of this order than the physicist, who often takes no interest in it.

There are good prospects of a *physics of integration,* a statistical integration of elements such as the unifying integration of elements making up more complex structures. Fresh prospects of a return to the determinism of microphysics suggest that this difficulty results from the barely perceptible individuality of physical particles which are all but unisolable from the space-time ambience of which they are accidents. Here we are at the very beginning of that organization which extends up to man. We should note at this point the precise significance of the complexification which ascends along this line from the infinitely small, where

81

complexity is relatively simple, to the infinitely complex of the human, while the passage from the infinitely small of the electron to the infinitely great of stellar space is far less rich in significance and value.

The Energy of Centration

Teilhard's phenomenology does not stop with describing the material conditions of complexification only. It tries to descover its laws. For Teilhard, this is a matter of a special form of energy. We know that he distinguishes *radial energy,* and *energy of centration,* from tangential or ordinary energy. This kind of energy seems to many physicists to have no connection with the scientific concept of energy. They see in it some sort of new attempt to identify energy with the spiritual, while materialist biologists see in it a new outburst of vitalism, an explanation of life in terms of an energy specifically different in nature from the forms of energy in ordinary physics. Now, when Teilhard speaks of energy, it is not to deny that all vital mechanics obey the laws of thermodynamics, the second principle in particular. If living forms create order and organization, they do so at the price of an expenditure of energy which contributes to the exhaustion of the energy of the world, to *an increase of entropy*. But for Teilhard, the determining factor in organization and integration is a variety of energy. This novel concept is very clearly substantiated by that branch of cybernetics called the *theory of information.* This idea—identical with those of organization, complexity, and information-value—now seems to be based on a special energy which is a *negative entropy*. The world thus appears as the seat of a process of organization which, while decreasing entropy locally, does so at the cost of a general increase of entropy, which marks the loss of cosmic energy. Along with the important energy in alimentation processes, we today commonly distinguish, in machines, a qualitatively much smaller energy of information, the quantitative importance of which, however, is considerable. So, too, in cerebral functions, the energy needed for cellular maintenance is much more important than the slight energy needed for the regulation of nerve activity. Yet, the latter is responsible for nervous fatigue and exhaustion.

Therefore, though Teilhard's conception of energy appears to traditional physics as hazy as his idea of the within of things, we see that it is, in fact, at the very core of scientific progress. Further, it is the essentially comparative mind of cybernetics, with its stress on the new ideas emerging from the facts of organization, which will give physicists, buried in their analysis, a little more of the synthetic mind, and render them more open to the problems of integration.

III

The Scientific Phenomenology of
Biological Evolution and
Human History

The Ascent of Consciousness and the Meaning
of History

We have given special emphasis to this scientific aspect of consciousness in its relation to organic complexity, because it brings to Teilhard's support irrefutable proofs taken from the physiology of integration, and particularly from brain neurophysiology. The idea of a scientific aspect of consciousness, while rejected alike by most scientists and philosophers in their refusal to recognize the connection between the materially objective and the spiritually subjective in the organic unit, is inevitable and inescapably posited by the discoveries of the psychobiological sciences. Times have indeed changed since, in reaction to the erroneous methodology of the mechanists, it was necessary, in the name of objectivity, to limit biology to the material. At that time, recourse to psychology for guidance hindered the progress of neurophysiology, which spent itself in a search for a soul where there was none, that is, in the localizable. Today, on the contrary, to refuse to give a cerebral account of the most important psychic operations is to impede the advance of neurophysiology. It is important to understand clearly that to proceed thus and to determine objectively the comparative powers of the animal and man is not to indulge in metaphysical materialism, but simply to present scientifically incontestable findings—the biological aspects of "oneness"—which, as science, leave complete freedom of choice for metaphysicians who propose to study this same being in its full ontology by methods which, though not scientific, nevertheless have quite as valid criteria of certitude. Therefore, we do not say: Science leaves room for freedom to be a philosophical materialist or spiritualist, but rather that it leaves freedom only where metaphysics does not affirm something irreconcilable to science, as was the case with mechanist materialism or the idealism of Plato and Descartes, and only where philosophical inquiry and truth do not force one along a compulsorily metaphysical line. In his law of complexity-consciousness, Teilhard describes reality as it appears in terms of a scientific explanation. There is no denying it, and it is very important to understand it and then see what there is of it that philosophy must retain.

The Meaning of Evolution

Thus far, however, we have attacked only one aspect of Teilhardian phenomenology. To see, as a stereotype, the inner formation of nature while looking at the within from outside is interesting enough, but this does not give nature its whole significance. That there are creatures more or less integrated and endowed with consciousness would be merely a curiosity if there were no relationship between them, if the picture of complexification were not *a recall of a history* of complexification. As a paleontologist, Teilhard is in a position to give to his phenomenology the dimension of *time,* to make, so to speak, a moving picture out of a stereotype. Because he grasps the real meaning of creatures, which the law of complexity-consciousness has given him, he can understand the *meaning* of evolution and history. Because he knows that the earth has a history, he can show us that the actual picture of the complexity of creatures is a relation of *dependence* in time. Animals are not a curiosity of nature. They are a stage in the spiritualization of life, a preparation for man.

Nothing is more opposed to Christian concepts than the existentialist thesis that the universe is absurd, that no thing has meaning, and hence that it is impossible for any good to come from that monstrous human freedom which has, by chance, appeared in a meaningless world. Such a conception is scientifically false and untenable. What Teilhard offers in his *scientific phenomenology of evolution* is the ascent of consciousness. In this, he is content to develop his scientific conception of evolution, which is too often taken for a materialist evolution denying the idea of value and affirming that the greater comes from the less through magical powers in the less. Nothing is more contrary to the science of evolution than Heraclitus's philosophy of becoming and perpetual change. To grasp the scientific significance of evolution means, for Teilhard, finding the meaning of spiritualization, of the rise of the concept of value, of the historically progressive realization of the different degrees of material being. For this, there is no need of adherence to some theory or other about matters involving evolutionary mechanics. It is not even necessary to say that evolution has finality, with man as its final goal. It is sufficient to say that it is the ascent of complexity and results in the most complex being of all, man, and that therefore it is a phenomenon with a meaning, regardless of its philosophical import. Fixism, which is philosophically tenable, does not account for this fact. In its view, the brute has no meaning in relation to man, and, like the workings of creation, depends on chance or on a creator. Fixism sees man as the most perfect of creatures. He is not at all the result of a drive toward perfection. Man is, therefore, much more a king of creation in the scientific conception of evolution than in fixism, which superimposes him on an inhuman universe.

If the fact of evolution is opposed to the thesis of an absurd universe, an understanding of its full meaning helps to correct the position of Marxist dialectical materialism, which, though realizing the importance of the fact of evolution and its human result, has not entirely grasped the real uniqueness of human being, and this leads it to exaggerate historical, economic, and social determinisms in relation to the freedom of the human person. Teilhard, because he understood in a scientific way the within of things, can situate man in his right place and say that, in man, evolution prepares to take on a new meaning with the introduction, for the first time, of freedom.

Again because of a confusion about orders of being, it is commonly said that Teilhard professes an evolutionist philosophy. And once again we must reply that Teilhard is not philosophizing. He is simply content to describe the facts as paleontology finds them. The old quarrel between fixism and evolutionism has

lost most of its meaning by now. Science has made a fixist phenomenology impossible. No one can any longer deny that the
different species appeared at different epochs, nor that, at least so
far as the vertebrates are concerned, creatures have appeared in an
ascending order of complexity. Since Pasteur, we know that
spontaneous generation does not exist in nature. There is some
logic in thinking it once existed, for, at that level, the more
complex necessarily came from the less complex. Anyone teaching a miraculous creation of life by God would indeed have to
suppose a material to be animated, and that could only be inert
matter. It is even probable that the efforts of biochemists will end
in creating life in the laboratory. But we know it will not appear
at the first attempt, that they will not synthesize, right off, a cell
or an amoeba or a human egg with the power of producing a
man. Both nature and the chemist begin with a synthesis of
elementary bodies from which they move on to simple organic
bodies. It took millions of years to produce life at the beginning
of evolution, so that a progressive complexification of pre-life
environment—where, in their own time, photosynthetic pigments
and concentrations of nucleoproteins became differentiated—
might have been the equivalent of our viruses. These are really
cell-parasites and incapable of independent life. But their early
counterparts could have had as their precursors those nucleic
germs which were a kind of living crystal, animating the pre-
biological milieu, reproducing themselves there and, little by little,
individualizing a part of their environment.

Probably, such a complex process occurred only once in the
history of the earth, and it gave rise to the virus and simple unicellular life. It is possible that, because of their peculiar structure,

some of these unicellular beings were able to exist independently before variously branching off, but their story is forever lost with the disappearance of their fossils. What is certain is that all complex being was derived from simple being, and that it was not formed by spontaneous generation. Direct formation, from the inanimate, of a frog egg or of a mammal is as unthinkable as the spontaneous generation of a full-grown mouse from the Monday wash! To think that a miracle of God could have had such an effect is to understand nothing of God and His creative presence in the world. By His creative act, things "are" what they are. That is, they have a "nature" in the precise degree in which they are conceived by the creative intelligence of God. Almighty God does not will to be free to do just anything. He wills precisely what is according to the mighty law of His thought: this world in complexification with man as the goal.

With respect to origin, as every biologist knows, a living thing always comes from a germ, from a living cell provided by one or two other living things. When there is sexual reproduction, the new individual is truly new in that it is the product of a fusion of two demi-cells of different genetic construction. But most often, the uniqueness is only relative in that the specific characteristics common to both the parents are preserved. Actually, however, nature demonstrates in *mutations* abrupt variations in structure of the gametes, which cause the appearance of new characteristics, generally of new lines. For scientific phenomenology, these mutations are indeed an evolution, change, a transformation of characteristics in the living being. But it is very important to understand the significance of the scientific fact of this transformation. There is by no means a gradual transition, a true transformation, in which one biological nature is changed into another; rather, a protoplasmic structure, probably in the construct of the nucleoproteins making up the genes, abruptly disappears through molecular alterations, causing the appearance of another structure. The species is, in a sense, transformed into another, but it is because the first acted as "prime matter" which, in disappearing, allowed the creation of the second. If we transpose all of this into paleontological terms (and we shall ignore the question of whether actual mutations offer a full explanation, though they are a logical, rational basis for an understanding of evolution), we cannot say, for example, that the monkey changed into man. This is something the fixists attribute to evolutionist thought with all the metaphysical materialist consequences following from it. It is true that Marxist popularizations declare that the primate was little by little changed into man through working in the group, which developed its mind in developing its language, but what they declare is not true. Man became civilized through group work only because, as man, he was the owner of a brain more complex than the brain of the monkey. If we want a picture of what could have happened, we must imagine a non-human primate undergoing a sudden transformation of its gametes, thus making for the appearance of a different creature, a man, the laws of genetics then explaining the isolation of the species, even though at the beginning there was only one individual. But this is something we shall never be scientifically certain of. Evolutionism and transformism, therefore, simply postulate on indisputable paleontological grounds that, in the line of descent of the non-human primate, there appeared another creature which was a man, and that this process was not a transformation of a nature, but the appearance of a new nature, not through any capacity of the less complex to produce the more complex, but through a using of the lesser to produce the greater. Only the philosopher is in a position to think out the precise metaphysical meaning of this phenomenon, of the way in which evolution is creative.

Thus, we see in what sense a reconciliation between fixism and evolutionism becomes possible. The latter expresses the scientific fact of the descent of species, one from the other, which is the only not altogether absurd way of understanding paleontology. Yet it is entirely compatible with the philosophical position of ontological fixism, the affirmation of the separateness of the natures and essences of each species. To put it more concisely, instead of saying that each species was directly formed by spontaneous generation, we say that its embryo had its birth in change in a previous embryo of a similar but more simple nature.[1] In the most important of all instances, that of the animal origin of man—which has excited so much discussion because it seemed to imply that the "improved monkey" could not have any but an animal soul, we see that the right conception of scientific evolution is perfectly reconcilable with this difference in nature. Man, as compared to the monkey, revealed his spiritual superiority from the very first, in his possession of a more complex brain.

[1] The lower species possesses germinally the qualities of the higher, because their natures border one another, but we cannot really say that there was any development of the germ. The germ suddenly became a reality.

The Origin of Man and His Characteristics

We know that the old saying, "Man came from the monkey," is false, if one thereby means that actual anthropoids were our ancestors. Anthropoids are, in fact, a lateral branch quite far removed from the human branch. Their study is interesting, because they are the animals closest to us cerebrally. But we must not conclude from that that an increase in a chimpanzee's brain neurones would make it human. The two have biological natures far removed from one another. The chimpanzee's brain is simply less complex; it is made of living chimpanzee matter. The advances of paleontology, to which Teilhard contributed so much, tended for a long time to isolate a particular branch of the *hominids* distinct from other families of the primates. The branch became detached from the common line a very long time ago in the tertiary period, and then evolved separately. The common ancestors of the ape and man, therefore, are undifferentiated pre-apes, small animals on the order of the rodent and the insectivore, as yet unspecialized. The evolution of the hominids is characterized by the weak specialization of their organs, which remained primitive and polyvalent (teeth, feet). In the series of ascending complexification, the process of hominization consists in the erectification of the body, and in the acquirement of permanent biped status, which frees the hands and which, by altering the facial and cranial dynamics, affords the cranial space necessary for the brain and for development of the face and forehead. All of this is in preparation for the really specific characteristics of man—a brain more complex than others—which will govern the use of the hand and the articulation of a language. It is probable that the preponderant factor was a series of mutations which increased in the developing embryo the division of neurones, but this in a distinct, zoölogical branch peculiar to the appearance of man.

We thus come to the notion that man did not spring suddenly from an animal state. Rather, a prehuman animal branch was isolated during a long preparation for his coming. Up until the final stage, man did not exist. What one finds here, however, is not some sort of ape, but a prehuman having in its chemical construction particular features orienting it toward human condition. There are and will always be many unknown factors here, but, right now, though we cannot say that a direct line of ancestry has been worked out—there is the question of lateral branches—we can say that creatures such as the primitive tertiary Oreopithecus and later the Australopithecus, the primate with the cranial capacity of the anthropoid, and still later the true prehuman (Pithecanthropus, Sinanthropus, etc.) with a cranial development midway between the anthropoid and man, belong to the human line. In virtue of the ordinary laws of evolution, we thus see a twofold, separate preparation for man: a remote preparation and growth of the prehuman, and the appearance of true man at one stage of this evolution. Thus, a steady evolution of complexification from brute to man is undeniable, but this evolution by successive stages of distinct creatures, each with its proper nature, in no way implies a continuity of natures. Within the bounds of this orthogenesis, of the thrust, that is, taken in the vitalist sense, in which man finally comes into his own, it is hard to say exactly at what point true man was born, not because of any continuity in the progress, but because we cannot know whether a given fossil once housed a truly human mind. Actual nature gives us only the chimpanzee level, and the chimpanzee is not a hominid. We do not know at what higher level a true hominid might have begun to function, nor what the psychic content was of a creature with a brain midway between that actually corresponding to the chimpanzee level and the human cerebral level. Would such a creature be a true man, or still an animal hominid? Even if, as in Vercor's story, *Les animaux dénaturés,* we were to meet such a creature in real life, it would be difficult to evaluate it, since it is possible to be a complete man without having a cultural language. The great majority of modern paleontologists feel that the Pithecanthropus-Sinanthropus was a man because, besides his capacity for making tools, he also made fire. However, neurophysiology prefers to reserve the name "man" for a creature with a present-day brain volume, which is the case only since the time of the Neanderthal or the Cro-Magnon man. It is only at that stage that orthogenesis organically terminated, and clearly at that time that mind incontestably showed itself in the cult of the dead and the magic arts. The difference between the two men, though perhaps not so distinct as was once thought, is based on the fact that Neanderthal man still lacked development of the prefrontal lobes, hence his brutish appearance. Science cannot, therefore, tell the philosopher and the theologian when true man appeared, what man was and what he was not, but it does prove that, in the hominids, there was a progressive, even if discontinuous, series of distinct creatures. Consequently, we can say that, despite the intermediate stages, man one day abruptly appeared.

The Mechanisms and Modes of Evolution

Everything in what has been called, in the pejorative sense, Teilhard's evolutionism, thus comes down to nothing but the simple objectivity of paleontology. This supposes no necessarily metaphysical propositions, or even taking a stand on debatable hypotheses in explaining evolution. Three factors appear to be involved, and none of them can be settled by vote. First, there are the properties peculiar to *living matter,* which, when one observes it by the proper methods, appears to be endowed with powers of self-change, one of the modes of this change having the signal privilege of true complexification, of the *ascent of integration,* of development of the cerebral organ. Some scientists, including Teilhard and Vandel, have stressed the role of internal factors. They were once criticized for being viatalists who postulated the intervention in evolution of a psychic, spiritual factor unacceptable on scientific grounds, for, it was reminded, science must deal only with properties of matter. But we have seen that, as a matter of fact, this psychic factor is a property of living matter. Evolution cannot be explained without taking account of all the properties of evolving matter, and it is likely enough that aptitude for complexification is one of them. May we not take the view that man was present in the potentialities of the spontaneous evolution of living matter, just as the adult is present in the genes of the ovum? Such a position is by no means metaphysical; indeed, it is a *de facto* scientific conclusion. To be sure, the realization of those potentialities of living matter could occur only in terms of dependence on environment. If such and such a creature appeared at such and such a time of

95

chronological evolution, when living matter was ripe enough, it could have been realized only if the environment was likewise ripe. A real *synthetic* theory of evolution must not neglect this internal factor. Unfortunately, that name is too often identified with the neo-Darwinian school, which is still based on a rather mechanist-materialist conception. In Lamarckism, the emphasis was squarely on *environmental factors,* though the part played by animal needs was also taken into account in explaining the organic *adaptation* secondarily determined by an heredity of acquired characteristics. This process has so far not been proved. Indeed, it seems that there is no necessity which involves change, but that the new creature appears completely equipped from the very first with its organs and instincts, the emphasis being on a characteristic in a line of growth which pertains far more to the spontaneous complexification of living matter following its own course than to the direct action of environment. This does not inhibit the play of environmental factors in the orientation of spontaneous evolution, in accelerating or retarding it. But we look to environmental factors not only at moments of mutation. They work especially to intervene in a secondary way, and thereby create the third factor in evolution, one which Darwin stressed—the *natural selection* which, in the struggle for existence, favors creatures better adapted to the physical and biological environment. This selective process certainly plays an important role, and neo-Darwinists believe they can explain all evolution in terms of it. That is, they contend that mutations come about quite by chance, either because of spontaneous variation, or because of the environment, but without meaning or finality. Finality depends on the secondary intervention of selection, in its rejection of the unfit and this is what causes progress. And man, the chance product of a meaningless evolution, owes his triumphant position only to his superior psychological faculties.

Though we do not deny the importance of selection, we do feel that such a view cannot adequately explain orthogenesis, steady progress in one direction, as this appears to be an orientated succession of mutations depending on an internal factor in living matter. The development of the brain does influence the struggle for existence, but if a more complex brain appears in one creature and not in another, this is due not to chance, but to a special tendency of living matter.

The Real Meaning of Evolution

We have seen that not all paleontologists agree that there is a *meaning* in evolution, and we said that this is due to the fact that they do not withdraw enough from detail to understand the full implication of the phenomenon. But we must not therefore conclude that, because there is one, main line of evolutionary ascent in complexification of creatures whose brain is more and more complex, evolution is a simple process consisting only of this single path. Indeed, those who believe that evolution reveals the meaningless, absurd expansion of life in process of endlessly perfecting uninteresting little details and resulting even in the hypertrophy of organs incompatible with life, are also correct. For anyone attentive to detail, evolution is either incomprehensible and meaningless, or else it has only provisory significance: an actually valueless complication of an organ in process. However, it is the personal duty of a paleontologist to search for meaning. Though there are useless complications, there are also very, very profitable complexifications—*adaptive* complexifications which allows the creature to live perfectly well in a given environment. However, such complexification often takes the form of specialization, that is, of a loss of adaptive potentialities which renders existence impossible when the environment changes, or which at least seems to put the adapted creature outside the main current of vital ascent. Genuine complixification occurs not in some organ or other, but in an organism and its integration, and it always starts from simple, rather unadapted forms. At any epoch, it is possible to make a *value judgment* on the status of the world of life. There are surviving species which represent what is left of the ancient masters of the world: highly adapted creatures most of whom have disappeared because of environmental changes, others which continue to exist while ceasing to be of much consequence. There were once the lords of an hour who flourished in every sort of aquatic, terrestrial, and aerial environment, but whose complexity wrecked any possible future. And finally, there are the little, much humbler, but better integrated species in whom mutations were not orientated by mere chance or adaptation, but toward true progress. It is not merely theoretical to say that a scientific phenomenology of evolution thus makes clear those great laws which living matter uses to advance nearer to consciousness and shows the hominid and man appearing in due time, when life had reached the needed ripeness, when the more elementary lines had already achieved the greater part of their astounding development, and the time of final burgeoning was at hand.

It was Teilhard who revealed this phenomenology of evolution, and who, in particular, analyzed the paleontology of human being so as to show how a species, appearing like any other, has nonetheless in the end revealed a special type of evolutionary tendency. Its first tendency is to branch off disparately, but, instead, and to the contrary, it tends to concentrate itself, to converge and ever realize in itself more and more unity in extension over the whole earth. We shall not dwell on this aspect. Our aim is simply to show that the phenomenology of evolution is neither a philosophy nor a scientific theory, but a description of something that happened. Of course, such a phenomenology cannot be limited to life. It seeks to know how life appeared on earth, and puts together cosmogenic theories which tell us of a complexifying evolution of the inanimate prior to the evolution of life. Certainly, a significant process of which we are the final result is going forward in our corner of the universe. Can we therefore generalize and say on scientific grounds that the world has had a beginning, and that it will end either through exhaustion of energy or through a mysterious reflection of energy in the Teilhardian sense? There are several scientific theories which attempt to answer this problem, but in the last analysis it seems that science has reached its limits, and can go no further. What precisely is meant, for instance, by an expanding universe? Is it only apparent? a local process? Could there be elsewhere other biological evolutionary processes analogous to ours? There is no certainty on this matter, at least not yet.

The Meaning of History

We shall, therefore, have to limit ourselves to the study of the earth, and its life, and especially to that new process which is the result of man's appearance there. The past is of interest to Teilhard only insofar as it reveals the future, and this, too, has become a fresh source of misunderstanding. Here is a paleontologist whom one is willing enough to listen to about anything up until the time of fossil man, who dares to explain pre-history as well as history and, further, to reveal the future to us. If the future were really foreseeable, and we did not see it, would this not imply that we have no freedom, and that we are the passive playthings of a vast world-process? And are we any more capable of standing up against it than the diplodocus did the encroaching mammals? Here again, more than ever, Teilhard needs to be explained. The question on which our discussion will center is simply: Can we, using the objective methods of scientific phenomenology, predict the future?

First of all, because Teilhard understood the significance of the phenomenon of man in evolution, he does not say what will be, but *what ought to be* if everything happens *normally* according to evolutionary norms. The climb toward man in biological evolution existed because life possessed the potentialities for it, but it succeeded only because environmental conditions allowed it to. This ascent in no way discards the vicissitudes, meaningless or not, of evolutionary detail. And it will be the same with the future. The meaning of the past extends into the meaning of the future, but its fulfillment, which could be normal, depends on factors which could be lacking. It may perhaps come about through hazardous and roundabout ways in which there may appear to be advance of a meaningless sort, or even a regression. However, Teilhard sees the ascent and its success as more than a mere norm. If there are factors which can work in opposition, they are of less consequence than the favoring automatisms. We are in a world which ascends and progresses in virtue of its special laws, of matter as well as of human initiation. Powerful as the contrary factors may be, they are only accidental contradictions of real motor automatisms. A metaphysician would say that in an evolving creation, the very fact of being in a created state prevails against the factors which aim at destroying or perverting creation. It would be impossible, short of Manichaeism, to posit good and evil on common ground, and to give each equal weight.

When Teilhard, after coming as far as man, continues his observation of the past, this does not mean he identifies history and paleontology, nor that he seeks to play historian.[1] But he states that, plunged in the oftentimes meaningless ins and outs of history, the historian and the sociologist fail to make the withdrawal necessary to see the true meaning of human history. They are, like most paleontologists as well, submerged in small detail. If, in a genuine biological spirit, one is going to grasp man and his history, one has to start with the *nature* of this creature who is the very crown of evolution. For millions of years, life complexified, passing, thanks to the brain's develop-

[1] There is no question of a "naturalist" view of history. Rather, history is seen as a natural extension of natural history ending in human nature. This continuity does not at all suppress the discontinuity belonging to the proper character of history in relation to natural history.

ment, from shadowy bioconsciousness to true consciousness. In man, there is finally realized a brain structure so complex that it becomes possible for a true mind to exist organically. Up to man, there was only biological history. With man, organic growth halts and gives place to *psychological* growth. For the first time, an organ admits of a boundless progress in behavior. For the first time, in a social species, thanks to the brain, there are not only fixed, inescapable habit-patterns, but also a power of technical and moral discovery allowing for perpetual progress. Over and above the values of the individual, though not independent of these, social and cultural values assume a specific character. Because of the general power for imitation afforded by the brain and language, there is always improvement, and it increases from generation to generation. For anyone thus pondering history since man's appearance as a consequence of biological evolution—in which the upward advance of the largest brain capable of real spirituality is replaced by a collective advance in the utilization of this brain to make it give of all its potentiality, to use it more humanly—there appears a guiding thread, a norm for a definition of the meaning of history. This meaning does not come from a more or less partial, subjective judgment of an historian settling on such and such more or less debatable criterion—personal freedom, the socialist state, the growth of the religious sentiment, or atheism. The psychobiologist knows what *true progress* consists of. He knows, too, that if this progress is normal, that is, if it is along the axis of normal development toward which countless automatic factors press, it is still not inevitable, because—if we define men in terms of his biological ownership of a brain—it can make him give of his human psychological best only under clearly defined environmental conditions. Man, as opposed to the brute, is extremely pliable; in him, innate factors of behavior are highly reduced. He must learn everything, get everything from environment. The latter, according as to whether it is favorable or not, will end in allowing the full flowering of human cerebral potentialities, or by hampering them. This is especially so of the normal man living outside the human social environment, which, through language, provides the means of thought. As an individual, a man is what his genetic constitution made him at the moment of conception. But this gives him potentialities which can unfold in very different ways, depending on conditions of life, first of pregnancy, then of the early years which give man his consciousness. The real differences between human individuals of classes or races are, constitutionally speaking, slight. What hides their basic equality are the educational conditions. These days, only the privileged can thus become wholly human. The rest appear inferior only because they have been disabled, where they have been put into a situation where normal existence is impossible.

Human Freedom

The psychobiologist can make a value judgment on any given human individual. This is not to make a moral judgment, for the individual is not responsible for what determines the beginning of his life, though later he can freely dehumanize himself, and this apart from any subjective considerations. In fact, the psychobiologist possesses the criterion of *genuine human value.*

It does not consist in healthy balance or healthy adaptation to a given society in which the individual is happy, or solely in cultural development. It consists in being completely human and in making a right use of the human brain nature has given a man. Moreover, the human brain is the organ not only of intelligence, but of judgment in the interests of *true freedom,* of choice, of the discovery of what is right. Above all, it is, on the social level, the organ of reverential *love* of others and oneself. In this respect, one could spend much time harmonizing sound cerebral balance with the moral precept: "Love your neighbor as yourself." To adhere closely in one's understanding to the moral law—that is to make a human use of one's brain. It is, therefore, at least in a general way, easy to tell whether an individual or a society is human. One can classify them from the standpoint of human values. In every society, even if primitive and cultureless, a minimum humanization is possible. But cultural progress contributes to an understanding of what is human by developing consciousness through the progress of knowledge and language. The primitive, who is a man and endowed with prefrontal integration, has a heart and judgment, but they are in bonds to the automatisms of habit and taboo, the more so since individual consciousness is still dim. However, all too often culture remains superficial, technical, a rational tool detached from real values. The civilized man, with his opportunities of acquiring greater heart and judgment than the primitive, is as bound to habit as he is. His consciousness is developed, but often in an egotistical (that is, neurotic) way, contrary to the sound cerebral balance which he achieves only in social relationships between equals respectful of one another's differences and freedom.

The most dangerous defect of contemporary psychosociological science lies in its refusal, in the name of so-called scientific objectivity, to make value judgments, or to judge anything in relation to man, not only in the concrete, but in relation to human nature, which is not only a metaphysical thing, but an organic nature.[1] Because of this, we are in danger of a sort of human government which an ethic foreign to science cannot countenance. If, on the other hand, we study man strictly in terms of what he completely is, from the viewpoint of a scientific objectivity which, again due to his cerebral aspect, is rediscovering the true dimensions of the human person, we shall then be able to guide his development in terms of its historical meaning, that is to say, to continue, while improving the use of the brain, in self-awareness, in freedom and love.

There are at present two systems of psychology. Traditional philosophical psychology affirms spiritual values, but seems on the one hand to ignore the fact that these essential values are only possibilities which man must have in order to develop by means of the requisite environment, and, on the other hand, to ignore the fact that man can learn how to opt for the good. This is a factor as wholly overlooked by the old, compulsory systems of education as by the modern liberal systems, in which a child is more like a plant carefully nurtured in a proper environment than a creature to be *formed for freedom and the use of a will.*

[1] This does mean we must standardize men and cultures, but to humanize them with due regard for their differences. We should especially guard against taking occidental prejudices for norms.

In turn, scientific psychology refuses to work with values, and shuts itself up among external details of behavior. What is needed is a true scientifically objective psychology of values and subjectivity.

As for sociology, here, too, objectivity consists in making no judgments except on the adaptivity of the individual. The sociologist will describe various societies in time and space and make notable analyses of basic social laws. But he will halt at asking whether there is a progressive evolution of social structures in human history making for a finer development of the human person. He declines any attempt at a social critique which seeks to clarify social conditions better adapted to meet the norm of what goes into the making of a true man. And precisely there is the properly human concern of sociology. Yet, it is a sociology which, because, through Engels, it is wedged in between Darwin and the dialectic of nature, has grasped only one aspect of the evolution of social structures taken in a humanizing sense. It is a Marxist sociology. Unfortunately, its attempt falls short because of its belief that civilization was caused by historical automatisms, and because it refuses, in a deviation which is oddly idealistic in an historical materialism, to start from the psychobiological nature of man, from the fact of his having the largest brain. Cultural, economic, and social factors are thus not considered means to a humanizing civilization—those means which traditional idealism neglected. They are proclaimed the very makers and builders of human consciousness. In this view, the full flowering of consciousness is not just more or less encouraged or discouraged, as the case may be, by society. Instead of being the very heart of incarnate human

106

being, consciousness is but a superstructure, a reflection of a totalitarian society with all-powerful rights over the creature it has made.

It is disquieting to observe how modern Christian individualism has so lost sight of the historical dimension essential to Christianity that, as a consequence, Teilhard's idea is completely misunderstood and likened to the Marxist idea. Well, it is said, if Marx put Hegel on his feet, one can also say that Teilhard "corrected" the Marxist meaning of history. In a world divided between the relativists who, in the name of the absurd, deny all historical meaning and know not what to do with their freedom, and the totalitarians who strip us of our freedom in the name of a deified meaning of history, Teilhard brings scientific proof that the world is neither absurd nor in chains. There is a meaning to history, but man is to choose it freely. It involves the personalization of man and society; the growth of true freedom, which is the knowledge and the exercise of law; the full flowering of the present potentialities in human nature; and the possibility of being ever more a better man, and this in freedom and in love.

The Noösphere

How, we might well ask, could the noösphere, toward which Teilhard sees the human race moving in a unified universe, have been so misunderstood? Some have tried to make a sort of freedomless, totalitarian anthill out of it. They simply do not understand Teilhard's ideas on personal excellence in group life. They see him as dreaming of a creation of a novel kind of integration, which will bring individuals into social union by making them cells in a new hyperconscious social organism. Though some sociologists have been attracted by the similarity between the social and the organic, a biologist will not make such such a mistake. To be sure, there are certain resemblances between society and the organism in the organization of their elements, but a difference in nature obtains. Social integration does not create a super-individual on the organic level. If the social concept is kept within due limits, it can only issue in the greater development of individual persons. This is something Teilhard never ceased to repeat. In his view, there can be a super-person only at the level of the Mystical Body and its Head, Whose members we are.

Teilhard's scientific phenomenology, in its flight across prehistory and history, inducts us in the essential. We find two successive stages: first, humanity differentiating itself and spreading over the whole earth, developing its intelligence and technical powers; then, upon the complete occupation of the planet and extension of technical means, convergence replaces divergence, and the realization of a unified humanity commences. In the first stage, ignorant man is compelled to bow to the automatisms of history. Teilhard is not obliged to analyze these, but, as in biological evolution, they are a matter of a tangled mélange of regressive and progressive factors the over-all result of which, on the human level, is progress. At the second stage, in turn, growing scientific knowledge gives man an understanding of the factors which make up history, and in particular helps him to realize what the true meaning of history is and what must be done to build the future. Man need no longer, if he chooses, remain in passive subjection to historical contingency. He can eliminate the regressive and apply himself to what is human in him. The natural mechanisms which have been operating since the beginning of evolution, and which involved man's ascent at the cost of an astounding waste of energy, can be replaced by human direction which will be far more to man's purposes. As Teilhard says, we have come to the point where unified, enlightened humanity *can now take the destiny of evolution into its own hands*. Teilhard is not prophesying in any vulgar sense. He is, in the name of the past and of the psychobiological essence of man, witnessing to a future geared to the meaning of evolution. There are ascending paths and descending paths. So his thesis in no way implies that we are not free to choose evil, to choose, that is, out of ignorance or folly, the very road to destruction. He does not mean that we have only to rely on natural automatisms; rather, he says, we have reached that moment when man must control both good and evil and the meaning of history. It is a time of liberation, of the birth of true freedom. However—and we shall return to this—Teilhard tends to believe that, in a created world which has fallen and then been saved, the possibilities for evil and human folly are limited.[1] But he does not at all mean thereby that

[1] Pius XII would seem to agree with Teilhard when he says: "For the first time, men are aware not only of their growing interdependence, but even more of their wonderful unity. It means that mankind will be more and more disposed to become the Mystical Body of Christ. Thus, the need for the Christian solution to so many problems which keep the world in unrest will appear ever more evident to men of good will" (*Doc. cath.*, April 13th, 1958).

knowledge of the meaning of history, the ascent to the noösphere, excuses us from searching for better means of getting there.

The present world is divided between those who have a knowledge of values and yet feel no need to seek for them, and those who deny values and yet try desperately to find they know not what. The true position lies somewhere between the two. For values are not things whose fruit we possess and enjoy merely, they are not some kind of cheap capital. The mere glimpse of them induces reverence. To reach them requires a painful, difficult quest, an endless searching without rest, albeit with an accompanying peace, since there is simultaneously knowledge of the goal in view and a wholesome fear of missing it. We must increase our effort, then, in the humane sciences, toward a thorough knowledge of all economic, social, and psychological laws, but in the context of their human meaning and with the aim not of building a scientific, totalitarian, technocratic society, but of providing all men with a human culture which will help them to be themselves the willing builders of that noösphere, which needs all men, no matter how different, for its completion.

We saw how Teilhard, on the scientific level, gave recognition to the existence of a special energy of centration. This energy is, in fact, an aspect of love, *an energy of amorization*. He sees "a universe freighted with love in its evolution." Here again, Teilhard is accused of blurred thinking. Love, a human value, which some too objective scientists contemptuously call sentimentality, has nothing to do with physical energy. Only a man shut up in anthropomorphism or trapped in his faith in a God of love can see love everywhere! And it is something of a paradox that here

110

Teilhard, the scientist, is right, and that the idealists and mechanists are wrong. A lengthy study could be made about the levels of love paralleling the levels of consciousness, since love is an aspect of integration. How many psychosociologists there are who will not admit that love, a higher form of knowledge, is the fundamental element in interhuman ties, sexual love being but a particular instance of it. How many there are who isolate human love, and who will not study its slow, evolutionary preparations at the animal level. But love is not just a social-interindividual matter. It is not just that group super-centration which gives unity to society and is to be the soul of the personalist noösphere. Love, as we saw, is linked to the highest integration of the individual, who must love himself within certain optimum limits if he is to be well-balanced. A universe in process of increasing integration is a universe of love, and the energy of centration is an energy of love. The attractions and affinities in atoms and molecules, as remote as they are from love, bear some analogy to it, just as their organization bears the dimension of a consciousness. One step higher, and we have the elemental love of life, vital egotism and the social affinities of the brute. The development of the nervous system grows and personalizes love the same as it does consciousness. The secret of sound balance and happiness, Teilhard tells us, is self-centration, then other-centration, and finally super-centration on one greater than self. Certain schools of psychoanalysis, following Adler, stress the healing value of interpersonal relationships in certain disorders, a phase of the social aspect of love in which Freud saw only the sexual terminus. He was right to identify libido with the vital instinct. Unfortunately, however, he exaggerated its relation

with the sexual instinct. More recently, Daim has emphasized
the neurosis-healing character of idolification. Those of us who
are Christians know well that the God Who is present in all
creation is the same God Who is in all men, and that, in dying
on the cross, He revealed that He is Love.

IV

Scientific Phenomenology
and Religion

From Science to God

Traditionally, a due regard for natural order has meant that when a human mind seeks to examine reality, it begins with scientific analysis of sensible data, and then passes on to the conceptual reflection of philosophy, which ultimately leads to some sort of theology. Is it legitimate, then—as Teilhard has been accused of doing—as it were to telescope this intermediate state and, dispensing with philosophy in the technical sense, to pass directly from scientific phenomenology to faith, a faith which, though orthodox, will nonetheless be more mystical and more empirical than discursive reasoning and theology? Some will say that this is fideism, comparing religious feeling with scientific knowledge, whereas the two are entirely separate domains which could only be united by philosophical reflection. Thus, the ordinary believer looks at sensible data in the light of his faith and finds it difficult to reconcile the two. What he needs is a catechism, that is, some elementary philosophical and theological reflection.

But Teilhard is in no sense a fideist, and his religion is genuine Catholicism, that is (according to the approach we have adopted here), a faith that has been rationally articulated. If he is no philosopher and reproaches the philosophers with being idealists out of touch with the facts, he fully realizes nonetheless that a philosophy is necessary. In the next chapter, we shall see how important the role of the philosopher is once scientific phenomenology, which at first sight seems to eliminate that role, has been established. But if we deal first with religion, it is out of regard for one of the most original and fruitful traits of Teilhard's thought. He leaves the philosophers and theologians their own field, in which he does not wish to meddle,[1] but discovers a new means of approaching religion, God, and the spiritual soul which does not require one to travel the conceptual road of philosophy. He does not, of course, deny that one must travel this philosophical road if one is to acquire specific knowledge of God and religious truths. But it is well known that this road is inadequate. How often are we reminded that our faith must not remain purely notional, but express itself in our lives, in steadfast loyalty to Christ, in reception of the sacraments, in mystical experience. What connection is there between this living faith which is the "Christian phenomenon," not in the superficial popular sense, but in the exact sense of introspective scientific phenomenology, and the scientific phenomenon? There is commonly said to be none. Being a priest and a mystic, Teilhard can testify to the affinity between the approach of the scientist and the approach of the mystic, often contrasting them with that of the philosopher.

---

[1] This has not hindered his philosophical and theological training from bearing fruit in the development of his over-all view of the scientific. Another biologist, Chauvin, has lately said that "science no longer has any right to retreat from the eternal questions" (*Dieu des Savants, Dieu de l'Expérience*).

While himself living a life of integral faith, Teilhard scientifically elaborates only the *natural aspect,* the human infrastructures of such a faith—whence all the deficiencies with which he is belabored.

But it is another aspect of Teilhard's vision which is particularly fruitful: He reopens the traditional approach to God through creation. The time-honored proofs were more philosophical than scientific, whereas for Teilhard science leads of itself to the true, living, personal God of love, the God of the mystics. His scientific vision, which is connatural to the modern world, leads not to the theoretical possibility of the existence of God, but to the actual reality of the living God, considered under a particular aspect. At the same time, it is as a scientist that he approaches the God of Whom he already has mystical knowledge.

It will be said that this is only the self-deception of a believer. But this is not true, by any means. For a Christian, God can never be a reality that is altogether separate, belonging to a wholly different order. God cannot be dissociated from His work, which would not exist without Him, without His secret presence animating it (for that is what creation is). If, then, in a scientific frame of mind, using scientific methods, we attempt by means of a scientific phenomenology to grasp the whole of reality so far as it is perceptible from this point of view, how can a Christian deny that (assuming our observation to be sufficiently judicious, searching, and prolonged) something of God will be found without any recourse to philosophy? Scientific phenomenology will discover in phenomena something which points to God, natural religion, and the natural aspects of Christianity, though the true, supernatural essence of the latter will elude it.

Since Plato and Descartes, we have been accustomed to divorce material from spiritual being, with the result that everything spiritual lies beyond the scope of science, and that science is therefore wholly cut off from God, Who is not its object. Now that science, thanks to cerebral neurophysiology, is spontaneously rediscovering the spiritual in its organic aspect, the only upshot seems to be materialism. But with a little reflection, it is easy to perceive that science is not materialist by its own nature. The matter of the body which science studies is simply the material or organic aspect of being, which is the indissoluble union of matter and spirit. Though science is a partial approach, from a particular point of view, to total being and cannot know the spiritual as such, it cannot fail to perceive the incarnate aspect of spiritual being. Thus, today it is impossible to deny man's spiritual superiority without also denying neurophysiology. Cartesian science, wallowing in extension and quantity, left it to philosophy to search for God; but a scientific phenomenology of the within of things, insisting on the qualities that emerge from them, on the immeasurable, on the essential, not the accidental, can reach religious truths such as those that are affirmed in particular by the Catholic faith, without abandoning its own ground and without the aid of philosophy. We do not mean to say, of course, that everything proper to the faith would somehow be objectified for all, believers and non-believers alike, for this would destroy the specific nature of the faith. Rather, the truths discovered by scientific phenomenology and the truths of faith would simply *converge*. Certain religious values will be recognized under their scientific aspect. This convergence will be of great importance to the Christian, providing him as it does with confirmation of what he believes. Instead of constraining his religion, science will provide the believer with further support. The believing scientist, especially, will be cognizant of the balanced unity of thought that will result. And Teilhard is the prototype of this kind of believing scientist. But for the non-believer, who does not have this certitude of faith, the unity of science and religion will always remain at most a matter of probable arguments incapable of inducing conviction. If any-thing, he will only be convinced that science and faith seem to agree, that there is an interesting convergence of the two. But even this should suffice to bring him to a study of religion, in revelation and in the Church, as well as of philosophy and theology.

In the usual meaning which scientific analysis and mathematics give it, there are no proofs or demonstrations of God's existence. But the man who follows scientific phenomenology clear through, in all its depth, will see that God is truly the Supreme Integrator, coming to him out of the coherent all of the created, and Whom it would be illogical to deny. Superficial analysis sees not a cell, but a physiochemical process, not an individual, but a collection of cells. The spiritual is not localized, but it is nonetheless ap-parent to him who knows how to see it in terms of the integrated being of a unity. No one today denies the existence of the soul on the ground that the scalpel does not reveal it. Even the non-believer, the man, that is to say, who does not believe in his own immortality, knows that the soul is not localizable. Some day, this will also be realized of God, the supreme, super-personalizing integrator. Scientific analysis of the whole of reality, when pressed to the limit, flows in on the living "heart" of this reality, which always eludes the mechanist and the rationalist. To know this "heart," however, requires acquaintance with it in other ways, through philosophy, theology, faith.

Contrary to what is often thought, Teilhard was not out of character as a scientist when, without contravening phenomenological principles, he joined that science with the God of the Catholic religion and theology, the superiority of which he thus demonstrates in a quasi-objective way. It may be that he went so far only because of his vital faith in God and his theological knowledge of Him, a God whose message is of full value only for believers. However, it is necessary to remember that in so doing, he did not stray from the axis of science, even in approaching God, and that, theoretically at least, any non-believer who consents to follow him must go the whole way to that mystery of love whose true reality he must learn and live. To try to separate the scientist and the believer in Teilhard would be monstrous. If Engels and Huxley did not end up in religion, that is because they did not follow their science and knowledge of nature through to the very end.

When Teilhard tells us, therefore, that he is dealing with the *whole* phenomenon, his venture can only end in God, in a *transparency* of phenomena so total that they reveal their real nature as accidents of being, that, consequently, one thus passes from the surface of phenomena to the supreme Reality. But let us say again that, if Teilhard speaks of God, it is strictly from the viewpoint of the central idea of his scientific phenomenology. It is thus a very limited view. Teilhard has never said that it was complete. It was not his intent to give us a *Summa theologica* and to tell us all about God. And if his ideas on the divine are in general poorly thought of by traditionalists, they are nonetheless of the greatest importance for modern apologetics. Hence, it is necessary, and even urgent, that we now work them out—it being taken for granted that the reader will see them in their proper perspective.

Though Teilhard's scientific phenomenology does not operate within the religious realm, it does completely differ from that separatism peculiar to the laboratory and the oratory, which separates the religious and scientific orders instead of simply distinguishing different viewpoints converging on a single reality. Thus, Teilhard agrees that science has worthwhile arguments to give religion, but rejects the concordism which intermixes levels of reality. We do not mean here negative concordism, which turns to the divine to supply what science cannot provide—Teilhard's God is the God of cosmic harmony, not the lord of the irrational and unintelligible—nor positive concordism, which is the refusal to identify scientific concepts and religious truths, to confuse viewpoints. Demonstration of human cerebral superiority is not a scientific proof of the immortality of the soul,[1] and the non-believer makes no scientific mistake in refusing to admit it. Likewise, there is no scientific argument proving the existence of God as such. Any such argument comes not from some isolated fact, but from an over-all picture in which, through plain, logical reflection and data and without metaphysics, the immortality of the soul or the existence of God become probable, and this can then be confirmed by proofs from the special standpoint of metaphysics or theology. God is like a watermark in the fiber

---

[1] The proof is the philosopher's business, but in a realist context it will be in agreement with science.

of existence (Loew), and one must know how to see Him. It is easier when one knows Him. A man standing flat on the ground has a certain right to deny, or at least to doubt, that such and such a piece of ground hides certain ancient ruins. But aerial photography can, for all that, give him irrefutable proof of their existence. Taken in its entirety, Teilhard's phenomenology is such a proof. But for it to be of any use, one will have to admit the existence, the value, and the possibilities of this phenomenology.

The God of Creation

The *Omega Point* has attained such notoriety that the God of Teilhard is often thought of as a God Who is to come, a God Who is in process, Who is the result of history, the ultimate convergence of which is to glorify matter. It was logical enough that the phenomenology of evolution should produce such a view. This spiritualization of the world where the one appears more often than not under the aspect of the many, where integration is in process, where the human race converges on an interdependent noösphere, is an ascent toward God, the focus of attraction. Teilhard understood very well how to distinguish, in the Omega Point, between what is human—the concord of the earthly city which is the sole aim of Marxism—and what is divine—the transformation of that city into the heavenly Jerusalem, which can never be the work of man. And he simply tells us that, *normally,* according to the essential meaning of history, human work, which sin alone can alienate from the freedom-creating grace of God, can reach such perfection that no apocalyptical cataclysm of destruction will be necessary, and that it is human work alone which will be glorified, that is, super-created. There is, then, one aspect of the Omega Point—the convergence of the human race—which both believers and non-believers can accept on objective grounds as something which will probably take place on condition that we will it. There is another aspect, however, which transcends this level. That spiritualizing convergence is possible only if a higher, attracting focus of spiritualization *pre-exists,* which the human omega invokes. The reflection of energy, the spiritual mutation of a world fleeing from death and the increase of entropy, is beyond the unaided resources of the world.[1] The intervention of something completely other is necessary. But both creation and grace are already consequences of it. Starting from science, Teilhard gives new meaning to Christian eschatology without damage to its fundamental definition.

It is important to emphasize, however, that the Omega is not an aspect of God. Teilhard has always said that God preëxists to the convergence. The world ascends only insofar as it is drawn to him. His God is the traditional God of creation, Who was, is, and will be forever and ever. Keeping in mind, then, that in the scientist's explanation of evolution, everything seems to happen with such apparent ease, due to the mechanisms he has discovered, and that his basic idea is that, for science, nothing exists which cannot be explained, remembering this we might ask: How is such a man to encounter the God of creation? How else, but that God's real face must be presented to him. In general, the truth of a Catholic dogma consists of the partial truths contained

[1] These resources are themselves the product of the world's created condition.

in contrary propositions of which it is a synthesis. The Church has justly condemned all those errors which identified God with the world while denying His transcendence, all the pantheisms and immanentisms. But to condemn those who say that God is only immanent and identical with the laws of nature is not the same thing as to reject the true proposition that the true, transcendent God acts by way of a hidden, animating presence, by way of immanence.[1] It is He Who, according to the laws of secondary causality, makes everything happen with such seeming ease. The Church, in fact, has just as wholly condemned the opposite error of pantheism, the idea of a transcendent God completely cut off from His creation, which He can act on only through magic. This is the God of gnosticism with its appeal to intermediary beings, of Manichaeism, which abandons the world to evil, the God of Islam and, to a degree, of Protestantism. It is not the creator God of Catholicism, Who is a God who respects the realm of the natural and its own integrity. Protestants sometimes mistakenly accuse Catholics of Pelagianism, of overestimating nature in relation to grace. This is not true. Catholicism rejected the error of Pelagius, who also separated man from God, grace from freedom, in order, as he said, to preserve man's freedom and power. But Catholicism retained what truth there was in Pelagius' exaggerated claims: Man is free, for freedom and grace are not mutually contradictory in him.

This is the authentic God Whom Teilhard presents as the one hidden in the many. If we understand Teilhard rightly, it is im-

[1] Hans Urs von Balthasar speaks of "panentheism." While his ideas on this matter are remote enough from Teilhard's, there is still a surprising convergence of the two (see, for instance, *Word and Redemption,* New York, 1965).

possible to accuse him of pantheism or immanentism, of taking the transcendent, the supernatural, grace, and the study of their natural infrastructures in terms of a naturalism which shrinks the transcendent. He is not writing a theological treatise. He only shows us God in the scientific order, His in-forming, spiritualizing immanence in creation, the divine milieu. In establishing the close relationship of integration with consciousness and love, he uncovers the secret of unity in the universe. This integration, which science defines as material organization, is not proof of materialism, but, on the contrary, appeals to a higher power of in-formation and spiritualization. The whole dialectic of nature ends in spirit solely because preëxisting spirit is its hidden animator. Evolution is creative only because creation is evolutive. Nature exists and coheres only because it is the presence of God. It ascends toward the Omega only because God sustains it. Just as consciousness or love preëxists analogically in man on down to the inanimate objects, which manifest these qualities according to their potentiality, so we cannot separate the creative God of nature from the God of supernature, from the God of grace and glory. We are not concerned with the mistake made in identifying nature and supernature, but with that of separating them. Man alone has the psychobiological capacity of being wide open to love and grace, and of having a supernatural life which puts him in special relation with God. God is not separate from natural life, but vitalizes it *to its core* with a new life.

The God responsible for the evolutive ascent converging on Him, the God secretly present in the hearts of creatures, by which only man can take up a personal relation with Him, this God of Teilhardian phenomenology is also—not the pantheist soul of the world, but the *personal* God, the *Love* of Christianity, and Teilhard gives very pertinent arguments for this truth from science. Since the universe results in the human person, it must be that the immanent, driving force in it is itself a person of a higher order. In the molecule, atoms lose their personal character through integration, and it is the same with the cells in our bodies. On the other hand, our nature as persons is not dissolved in a social super-creature. All of this shows that there is truth in and a need for supposing an over-all integration of mankind leading one to postulate an integration superior to the personal level, and capable of being at the same time immanent in and transcendent over it. This is precisely the nature of God's relation to us. He is in us more intimately than we are ourselves, but He remains of another order and unites us in the Mystical Body of which He is the Head.

So far as the human soul is concerned, beyond the belief in its immortality and the arguments of philosophy which establish the belief, there is a possibility of certain other scientific arguments from nature. Modern science has established the fact that the superiority of human nature is no illusion. And it indicates that we cannot deduce the non-existence of a different metaphysical nature from the man-animal analogy. In these circumstance, the special qualities of the human psychism—powers of reflection and abstraction, a capacity for metaphysical reasoning, for knowledge of the universal and of being—seem to indicate, indeed, a peculiarly spiritual nature whose dependence on God is of another order. As Genesis expresses it: God created man in His own image.

Christ, the Angels, and Satan

Scientific phenomenology not only encourages us, therefore to affirm the possible harmony of science with faith; it also shows us, objectively, that the truths of faith are scientifically probable. One last aspect only remains to be set forth—not evil, which we will discuss later in a special chapter, but Satan. The Christian vision of the world emphasizes one particular moment of history, the Incarnation of God, the historic life of Christ, the Man-God. Very properly, the Church links this important event with original sin and the necessity of the redemption. As a scientist, however, Teilhard is not concerned with the redemption considered as the restoration of man to the supernatural life. But, if this is so, can he then sketch for us a picture, in historical, eschatological terms, of a lone *élan,* an unfallen nature, converging toward God? We will see that, in fact, we must take original sin as proof not of the original cultural superiority of man, but rather of his very weakness,[1] and this is in accord with the point of view of science. On the other hand, original sin, which above all is concerned with the supernatural life, did not bring about an absolute break in the natural order of history. It is a factor contributing to deviations and retardations rather than to a recessive and utterly destructive process. It has become more difficult for man to understand and realize his nature. And it is precisely here, once more, that Teilhard, from a scientist's viewpoint, becomes the defender of a level, an infrastructure of natural continuity, the point where we saw only the superstructure of a

[1] A weakness, yes, but a greatness, too, in terms of responsible freedom, out of which stems a blindly unaware pride leading to sin.

break, of supernatural discontinuity. Thus, he asks himself, as regards this continuity, whether Christ, over and above the redemptive role indissociable from Him, has not His natural place in the dialectic of history.

In his answer, Teilhard, writing in the language of science, comes up with an unusual idea, but one which joins with certain traditional ideas (Duns Scotus, for one)—the idea of the *evolving Christ*. Christ is not merely an aspect of the Omega Point, the Christ of the Parousia, the coming glory of the human race. He is Himself the union of the human race with divinity. He is not only the universal Christ, the Head of the Mystical Body. As Christ, the historical redeemer, did He not have His natural place in God's design, that is, in complexifying, spiritualizing, material evolution? Just as all biological evolution was man's painful childbirth, the full meaning of the evolving phenomenon and its justification seem to demand that the spiritualizing process be such that God be able to come freely and take his place in it, not as Omega Point, but as a man appearing at a moment in history which, seemingly commonplace, must yet be enough delayed to allow civilization and religious thinking to be sufficiently advanced and ready for it, yet early enough to afford a new beginning, the founding of the Church and sacramental sanctification. The closer presence of God was needed in a world wandering in materialism, idealism, and magic. That organic creature, man, so weak that he became a sinner, yet intelligent enough to be responsible for it, needed not only the presence of God's love to help him. He had also to find, in some way, a rational justification, by an argument from convenience, for the folly of evolution—that apparent ascent of nothing toward the condition of something—by showing that the jewel of evolution was precious enough to be *saved* by the folly of the cross. In the natural act of original sin, man cut his supernatural ties. Christ, in His natural insertion into the human race, restored these ties. How dear the natural is to the supernatural!

Can a cosmic union, such as Teilhard's, which does not halt at integrating God with evolution, be complete without taking the angels into account? As we have said, Teilhard is not bound to cover everything. He is content to throw new light on whatever falls within the central focus of his thought as a scientist. By definition, angels, spiritual creatures, are not the concern of the scientist. As a Christian, Teilhard simply holds that these pure spirits, whose existence the Church assures us of, cannot act on us in any other way than God does, that is, by way of a trans-conscious immanence which we are unable to discern among all those secret motivations of ours. It is not difficult, therefore, for us naturally to include the angels as *co-evolving* creatures. Indeed, this has the advantage of allowing us to include Satan, the fallen angel, logically in the Teilhardian concept. While Teilhard admits, with the Church, the existence of evil so great that it is personified in a being superior to man but less than God, we will see that as a scientist he gives very little attention to this problem.[1] In relation to the evolving Christ, we might, for completeness' sake, consider *Satan as in-volving* in terms of a regressive drive. It is for the theologians to tell us whether the first angelic

---

[1] So, too, the scientist has no obligation to deal with hell, which is not so much a place of punishment as a state of revolt in the soul such that frustrated love burns it—that same love which, when accepted, glorifies the elect and purifies them in the purgatorial state. This is in perfect harmony with Teilhard's view.

sin, which gave evil its concrete character, was not quite simply the pride of the idealist rejection of this material evolution of complexification in which God Himself, as man, was to be included. This was the sin of Satan, which led, at the very beginning, to that fleshless idealism with its contempt for the flesh, and then to the shackling of the flesh in ungoverned materialism.

If we have here chosen to go even further than Teilhard to these far limits of discussion, it was only to show how fruitful such meditations on the results of his phenomenology can be for theology. There are in Church teaching certain truths of the greatest importance for the modern world, and which that world rejects because it has taken a ridiculous attitude toward them. Its idea of the devil is a good example. Because a true, Judeo-Christian conception may have become tainted with a certain amount of Babylonian imagery, this does not make it false. It only needs to be purified in order to recover its full truth and force, and for this task, nothing could be more useful than to see how the devil has a natural place in the phenomenology of the within of things and of evolution. There are two mistakes we must remember not to make: slighting the supernatural, and forgetting that the supernatural is inserted into the natural, which it does not destroy, but super-vitalizes. Teilhard has answered a great need in affirming the natural, so that, as a consequence, we are duty bound not to reproach him for what he had done, but rather to join with him in declaring that this question, too, comes within the purview of science, however limited that view may be.

V

Scientific Phenomenology and Thomistic Philosophy

We have reached a point where we can positively state that Teilhard de Chardin is neither a philosopher nor a theologian in the traditional and, so to speak, technical sense of the word. He is a scientist whose distinction is to have developed a synthetic interpretation of an aspect of science which many scientists, because they lacked the synthetic mind, did not discover, even though that is the essential and principal aim of science. To be sure, the synthetic mind is eminently the philosophic mind. But to be a philosopher requires more than a love of synthesis; the exercise of a special type of conceptual thinking is also required. Teilhard's philosophical mind is exclusively devoted to science. Similarly, the religious mind of Teilhard, a man of faith and a priest, shows almost the character of growth along the main line of scientific, synthetic thought, though it affords him the certitude of rational faith which every Catholic instructed in his religion has. So, when Teilhard enters the religious field, he is not speaking as a theologian. He simply observes there certain aspects which agree with his science, elements of natural religion which even a non-believing scientist may come to see strictly from the viewpoint of introspective, scientific phenomenology; or matters of more specifically religious values whose essence remains outside of science. These Teilhard, ever keeping his character as a man of faith, yet always regards with a scientific eye, from the viewpoint of matter as a conditioning agent. He thus brings forward important aspects often overlooked by idealist deviations of religion, aspects adapted to the vision of modern man in a scientific, technical world, aspects, too, from which the modern draws atheistic or anti-Catholic arguments, but which Teilhard demonstrates to be in agreement with traditional faith.

However, if we are to understand and use Teilhardian thought, we must understand the fact that, while it is complete as a scientific phenomenology, it is by nature incomplete as an explanation of the world. And we will repeat once more that, in nowise a philosophy or a theology, Teilhard's phenomenology does not pretend to substitute for either, or to make esssential changes in them. It does require, however, that philosophy and theology pay more heed to their immanent relationship with science.

Many a philosopher has risen up against Teilhard to say that his thought is only partial, that he seriously distorts philosophy and theology, even though he has produced some interesting new ideas perhaps a little too unregarded these days. They are perfectly correct in calling him incomplete. But if he was, it is because he wisely kept within his field. He is incomplete, because phenomenology is incomplete. He is not incomplete because of philosophical or theological incompetence. It is of little importance what his personal philosophical or theological training was, or what did or did not interest him in philosophy or theology. He had no specific need of these in his work, not because they are useless, but because phenomenology does not work in terms of philosophy and theology. The men who succeed Teilhard to develop his phenomenology further will be in a position to uncover certain other aspects which, some day, will seem less off-course for traditional thought (the neurophysiology of freedom and sin, for instance). But this will not make them philosophers or theologians.

Though it is in the nature of Teilhardian phenomenology to pass directly from the scientific to the religious, Teilhard was not interested, on the other hand, to make connections between his phenomenology and philosophy. And this is work which urgently needs to be done today in order to enlighten and reassure philosophers. To start with, we need the services of scientists who can show clearly the relationship between scientific phenomenology and philosophy. It will then be for the philosopher to offer his viewpoint on this problem of intellectual frontiers. Scientific phenomenology is, in fact, only a *necessary introduction to traditional cosmology,* its scientific aspect developed in terms of scientific language and method. This scientific explanation of the world must then be matched by a *metaphysical, ontological explanation,* which is the work of philosophers employing their own terminology and working methods—traditional, philosophical cosmology. The two cosmologies must be closely welded together, for we are dealing here with a single reality whose explanation requires both science and philosophy. So while scientists and philosophers may work independently at first, it is necessary that each have a working knowledge of the other's field, and take his place among the intermediary thinkers

131

who possess both methods and both terminologies—incomplete cosmologists. This Teilhard was not.

Finally, we must abandon the idea that reality is double, that we can split it up into two realms, one of *matter,* the scientific, and one of *spirit,* the philosophical. Reality is one. Science and philosophy do not have different *material* objects; they are basically only different points of view of the same reality. By definition, science, when pushed to its limits, sees certain aspects of the real which are specifically the study of philosophy. Science does not know them in their entire dimension, but it is capable of discerning an aspect of their being. So, too, the philosopher does not dwell in a sky of concepts. Indeed, his concepts are true only if they keep in steady communication with concrete reality. Thus, when scientific phenomenology turns without hesitation to a philosophical vocabulary, it is entirely justified in doing so. Nothing would prejudice cosmology more than to differentiate by two different names the scientific aspect and the metaphysical aspect of the same phenomenon. There are uniquely philosophical considerations, such as the metaphysical principles of being—matter, spirit—which are not to be confused with the real being, the composite. And there are purely scientific considerations—organization, integration—which must not be confused with form. There remains the question of showing the relationship between these two orders of values. On the other hand, there are considerations at once philosophical and scientific which sometimes present two slightly contrary aspects: consciousness, the within of things, interiority. The scientist owes it to himself to beware any totalitarianism by presuming to deny the importance and the specific nature of the philosophical aspect, but the philosopher, in turn, must not deny the scientific viewpoint and take it for a poor, defective philosophical system.

It would be interesting and very worthwhile to compare scientific phenomenology with the various philosophical systems, on condition of not identifying Teilhard's concepts with philosophical propositions. Their convergence would be relative solely to the unity of the real as seen under various aspects. The close relation and intercourse between Teilhard and Le Roy are well known, and there would be a good deal to discuss about the analogies and differences between Teilhard and Bergson.[1] Father d'Armagnac has pointed out an affinity with Blondel. Not being a philosopher, we will be content here merely to indicate the close relationship between Teilhard and the "traditional" philosophy of the Church, *Thomism*. Biological phenomenology, which is closely related to Bernard's[2] scientific philosophy, as we said, harmonizes quite naturally with the realism of *hylomorphism*. It is mainly to Sertillanges, therefore, as a Thomist thinker, that we will turn, for it is Sertillanges who has best assimilated modern biology with traditional Thomism by showing to what degree Bernard and St. Thomas agree. It is he, also, who, in a book such as *L'idée de création,* so capably explained the relationship of a creator to his creation. It is, however, a joy for the biologist to find Daujat working out the possibilities of agreement in Thomism and modern physics.

To show Thomist philosophers and the Church that Teil-

[1] See the reports and discussions of the Bergson Congress (Paris, 1959).
[2] It would be interesting to discuss the nature of what Bernard calls the "directive idea" which science discovers in organisms.

hardian thought, so solidly established on scientific fact, yet apparently so baffling and unacceptable to them, is but the scientific aspect of the metaphysics of being, is surely a very useful undertaking if it puts an end to the misunderstandings about Teilhard.[1] We feel very strongly about this point. It is from a certain Thomistic milieu, very often, that an immense over-cautiousness, if not downright hostility, arises concerning Teilhard. Yet, the true realist spirit of St. Thomas was ever open to new ideas while remaining solidly anchored to tradition as guarantee against any distortion of doctrine. This was what helped St. Thomas to adapt and correct Aristotle and yet avoid the errors of Arabian and Jewish Aristotelians. This realist temper of Thomism is especially in harmony with Teilhard's scientific phenomenology. True, St. Thomas in thinking over the science of his day—Aristotle's—erected a cosmology far removed from modern science. Nevertheless, the main principles he applied remain valid, because they were philosophically true. Is it not strange, from the point of philosophical certitude, that the philosopher who best understood the relation of body and soul, Aristotle, had, even for his time, only very imperfect ideas about neurophysiology, ideas far inferior to those of Democritus, while a philosopher so fine a neurophysiologist as Descartes, on the other hand, taught ideas about the relation of body and soul that are absolutely unacceptable?

To bring about this confrontation, without any thought of twisting either his own thought or Thomism—that is to say, to

[1] This does not mean just that scientific phenomenology is reconcilable with Thomism. Something much more important is at stake here: the way of seeing the relationship of body and soul, of man and the brute.

sketch the possibilities for philosophers, is something which, unfortunately, Teilhard himself did not undertake.

However, it can be said that we have his authorization to do so ourselves. In fact, we find this note in his *La vision du passé* (1926): "Perhaps one could say, in that sense, that Aristotelian hylomorphism represents the projection of modern evolutionism on a world without duration. Transposed to a world to which duration adds another dimension, the theory of matter and form becomes almost indistinguishable from our present speculations about the development of nature."

In appearance and at first sight, Teilhard's work could pass for materialism, but a materialism which, in its dialectical flight, ends in the transcendent, personal God and in love, without any flaw or inner deviation resulting from its change of direction. It is a paradox which will not be avoided by saying that Teilhard, in his faith, super-adds God to his scientific vision, or that his God is a non-existant, pantheist world-soul. We have seen that it is the God of Catholicism, and that this concept can be naturally included in Teilhard's system, though it at first appears to be related to Engel's dialectic of nature. This God Who, in Marxist eyes, is wholly opposed to the coherence of the created in evolution, to human freedom, to the work of liberating the oppressed, becomes for Teilhard the sole justification of these very values. Where Marxism says that the growth of scientific materialism will destroy religion, as all rationalist scientists say, Teilhard shows that this apparent materialism, rightly understood, leads to God, but to the true God Whose being theology defends.

The division between science and religion is due to the fact that science grew up in a climate of mechanist definitions of a world in which spirit, isolated by idealist Platonic and Cartesian philosophy, could reappear only as a secondary production of matter, while philosophy and religion were compelled to confine themselves to a disincarnate spirituality which cut God from the world and the soul from the body. Marxism, in its faithfulness to science, seemed obliged to develop a materialism which has become more and more realist, that is, freer of the original mechanism and more cognizant of some specific nature in different levels of organization: molecule, life, man. But while this was taking place in a philosophy which continued to be materialist, spirit, though less underplayed than before, appeared more and more as secondary to matter, and it was to the latter's properties that the entire complexifying evolution of the world was attributed. Because philosophy was weak, the interpretations of science appeared strong, leading to the conclusion that metaphysics was non-existent, that is, to a negative metaphysics. This tendency is reinforced by a false conception of the relation of spirit and world, the belief that all spirituality, all theology, are necessarily an idealism which destroys autonomy and unity. But such a contention can be made only by one who is ignorant of true Thomist philosophy.

In his seemingly materialist phenomenology, Teilhard agrees to the factual schema of the materialists, but he draws, from his philosophical and theological thought, completely opposite conclusions.

Teilhard's vindication is in need of philosophical study which will account for the apparent materialism of his science, and show how it does not at all lead to metaphysical materialism, but that it agrees much more logically with that *realism of matter* which Thomism stands for. Moreover, it could be demonstrated that Teilhard is opposed to the idealist alienation of a "separated" God, and that his thought harmonizes perfectly with the true God Who animates from within, and Who, while respecting the autonomy of His creation, is yet not so identified with His work that His immanence impedes His transcendence.

The whole difficulty in the dialogue stems from ignorance of the object of science. One thinks of it in terms of matter, and gives this ordinary word the meaning of something constituting the real as opposed to spirit. Human thought, groping toward the truth of dualism with distinctions between matter and spirit, naturally comes to reify matter and spirit, to separate what is of the body from what is of the soul. Plato and Descartes are immanent in spiritualist and even materialist modern thought, for the materialist, too, is tempted to reify thought by making it a product of matter and something apart. Now, the business of science is not with matter as separated from spirit, or productive of spirit, or controlled by spirit, because, in reality, spirit and matter do not exist separately. There is only *one* reality, organized matter, which affords evidence of spirituality to the degree that matter is organized. Organization is the material aspect of the spiritual, in the same way as the spiritual is the specific aspect of organization, and no one can dissociate the two aspects of the unity of being by any amount of scientific study. The material object of science is, therefore, the same as that of metaphysics. Real beings are involved here, together with their degrees of being and their analogies. That which forms the specific nature of science and its phenomenology—that part of science which, in recomposing the whole, is concerned precisely with being as dissected and therefore destroyed by the individual sciences—is not its material object, but simply the point of view and the method with which it approaches its object. It is a matter of the material, organic aspect of being, a partial aspect of the whole being. It must, therefore, encounter spirit in its incarnate aspect, and judge of the analogy of beings by comparing their organic aspects, that is, their degree of integration, their organic condition at the level of interiority and consciousness—in other words, the organic aspect of these values. Because scientific phenomenology speaks of consciousness, its specific character in relation to philosophy is denied. It is said to have no proper object. It is without a proper material object, but it is, nevertheless, specifically distinct from philosophy, because the common object, being, is studied from a particular point of view and by particular methods.

But it is not enough to say that science is concerned with being. Rather, it is concerned with *created* being. It is impossible to isolate God from His work. Whether one believes in him or not does not alter the nature of things which involve the hidden presence of God. This presence may not intervene as an active force, but it does explain the reason for the extraordinary spiritualizing potentialities of the dialectic of material nature. It is not only that matter is indissociable from the spiritual factor which organizes and complexifies it. It is that this matter is created, and that all its powers and apparent autonomy come to it from the hidden presence of God, without Whom no thing would exist.

Common notions see the metaphysical idea of creation as little more than an initial flick of the finger needed to give creation a start. It would appear that God was necessary only at the beginning of things, or at certain crucial moments when a bit of superanimation was needed. Thus, a sort of concurrence between God and nature is established, the first cause being necessary whenever secondary causality flags. Material complexification would be the work of the mechanisms of evolution, but for the passage from matter to life, from brute to man, God would have to intervene. Under these conditions, man is separated into a body supplied only with the powers of evolutive, material complexification, and into a spiritual soul created directly by God. As for the brute with only a material body and no real soul, evolution suffices to produce it.

Now, the Christian truth about this matter is something else altogether. The creative act entails the constant and total dependence of creation[1] on the creator. The latter acts through the apparent autonomy of secondary causes such as phenomenology is able to discover. But without His permanent action, everything would disappear into nothingness. At every moment of evolution, the metaphysician, with due regard for degrees of being, places God above (and yet at the heart of) secondary causes. This animating presence of God has degrees: There is more of creative activity, therefore more of the spiritual, in the living being than than in the inanimate, in man than in the brute. But this in nowise prohibits scientific analysis from saying that, from its point of view, life comes by animation of the inert through spontaneous complexification, or that structural rearrangements in the ovum of a pre-human primate produced living human

---

[1] And therefore of freedom as freedom and chance as chance. Neither freedom nor chance is contrary to God.

matter the complex architecture of which reveals the superanimation. Everything springs from complexification, but this complexification is the incarnation of the spiritual. To say that the living thing is more complex than the non-living is only to formulate scientifically the metaphysical conception that the vegetative or animal soul is superior, but analogous, to substantial form. To say that pre-human complexification produced man in all his animated being is the same as saying that God specifically created the human soul. From the scientific angle, evolution produces all creatures, apes and men, and produces them complete, with their proper psychism conditioned by their organization. But this scientific angle does not eliminate, indeed, on the contrary, it invokes the metaphysical analysis which shows God at work in evolutive mechanisms. The scientist describes the material aspect of analogies, where the continuity is very clear despite the marked discontinuities between the lon-living and the living, between brute and man. This does mean that the scientific aspect exhausts the notion of analogy, of which it is only the infrastructure, the lower, though a principal, aspect. It is for the metaphysician to explain what this analogy (which the scientist sees only one aspect of) consists in. In doing so, he must show how the small but significant material discontinuities of science between inanimate and living, especially between man and brute, denote, in fact, *formal discontinuities,* metaphysical differences. But this should not lead him to deny the material realities of scientific phenomenology.

As for what the metaphysician tells us on rational grounds, that only man has a soul capable of a special existence apart from its power of animating the body—its hidden, immanent presence in an indissociable composite—it does not follow that this soul in its proper dimension is in the body otherwise than by in-formation. Despite its superiority, the human soul behaves organically like the brute soul. But it makes for a higher integration, for a larger brain which allows it to exercise its proper spiritual qualities in life. Like phenomenology in its use of the word "consciousness," which it must employ to convey realities analogous to real human consciousness, metaphysics too is cramped by terminology. Man is the only incarnate soul; his soul alone bears an analogy to God or the angels sufficient to justify the name "spiritual," even though this spiritual aspect is the integrating force of a molecular dust of cells which gives it a "material" aspect. The animal soul, which has this aspect only, cannot be characterized as spiritual. Nevertheless, we must firmly maintain the analogy between this principle, non-existant outside the composite, and the human soul, an analogy which implies a certain inferior, elementary degree of spirituality. The ascent of evolutive complexification is a spiritualization of nature under the influence of the creator, a spiritualization which debouches in true spirit only in man, but which is nonetheless an ontological complexification necessary for the organic conditions which permit incarnation of the human soul.

Thus, we see that in the midst of the incertitudes and contradictions of dialetical materialism and idealism, Thomist philosophy[1] and its hylomorphism can provide us with an exact synthesis, because it preserves the unity of being. It does not separate spirit and matter, body and soul, brute and man, and is able to recognize that this unity overlays distinct metaphysical

[1] Which grafted Catholic spirituality and the truth in Platonic idealism on Aristotelian realism.

realities. To affirm formal discontinuities is not to deny material
continuities or of the material aspects of formal discontinuities
where the latter are revealed only incompletely. The modern
phenomenology of the within of things finds its metaphysical
justification in Thomism. It receives authority from it to give
matter and body their proper place, since, for the scientist, matter
and body are the material, organic aspect of a composite involving
the immanent presence of a soul or form. There is regrettable
confusion in having to give the same name to two different
realities, and the need for clarification, though difficult, is urgent.
The word "matter" means sensible being, which is ordinarily
thought of as inanimate, whereas it is only less animate, that is
to say, the composite of *in-formed* matter. It also means the principle of matter, which philosophical analysis isolates as a principle
without independent existence. When the scientist speaks of
matter, on the other hand, he thinks totally to exclude spirit,
whereas form, as elementary and inchoative participation in
spirituality, is an essential principle of sensible spirituality, and so
he is wrongly called a materialist. The philosopher, in turn, speaks
of this principle as opposed to spirit, and thus he cannot understand the scientist. It is the same with the body. The body is not
a machine at the service of a soul. It is not matter, since matter is
a metaphysical principle which the scientist never encounters. It
is a composite, animated matter, from which the soul is inseparable, for at death the soul is not separated from the body. The
composite simply breaks up. Where the soul continues in existence, there is no longer any body, but a *cadaver,* a molecular dust
committed to dispersion. Thus, the organic aspect of the human
spirit, which modern biological psychology is increasingly en-

countering because a science of the body cannot exist without the soul immanent in that body, is given adequate explanation. To say that science is concerned with the body is to express its concern with the organic aspect of the whole being. But metaphysics, too, is concerned with the body in its ontological aspect, with showing us its constitutive principles. When there is question of the soul, there is no difficulty. But when the material principle becomes involved, one adopts the disastrous practice of so describing the body, the composite, that the body becomes opposed to soul. Man is not made of body and soul as of two equal principles. He is an incarnate soul, a soul which is the principle of bodily integration, and in this body only the integrating spiritual element is important as bestowing its dimension on human being. Incarnation simply means that the soul appears in a condition of material organization. Therefore, that which must be added to the human soul to produce the composite, the body, is not a human principle. It is common matter with its elementary organization, which the soul takes under its responsibility.

Thus we see in what sense the meeting of Thomism and scientific phenomenology is useful for giving a complete realist picture of the world in process of becoming. Everything which might have seemed materialist or pantheistic in phenomenology, everything which seems to magnify the spiritualizing capacities of an independent matter, is conceived in a spiritualist sense, because it is a question of in-formed matter in a state of creation, of an historical development of essences and their potentialities.

As Teilhard said in the note we recalled, the only change of any real importance since St. Thomas is that we have learned about the role of the time factor.[1] This factor is very important for a precise statement of the conditions of the development of creatures, but it alters nothing in their nature. St. Thomas had adopted a sort of stereotype of nature, understanding quite well the comparative progression of various states of being and guarding equally well against falling into idealist separatism. Teilhard, with the paleontological facts of evolution, is able to bring the stereotype to life, without this significant change altering the metaphysical meaning and values of creatures. Created nature only becomes more unified and meaningful in its ascending convergence from the many to the one.

All of the alleged philosophical incompleteness of Teilhard stems from his not speaking like a philosopher, and his not having had, as a scientist, to make an ontological analysis of the unity of being. Today, it is quite possible (it is absolutely necessary) to emphasize the analogous continuity which nature presents, a sort of ladder of biological natures, to emphasize at the same time, therefore, the similarities and differences of man and the animal, without at the same time being obliged to deny the complementary viewpoint of the formal discontinuity which gives man his real spiritual stature. Science is perfectly correct in tracing the roots of the human psychism from the lowest rung of animal life. There has been no progressive development of a germ, but a fulfillment of more and more complex beings.

[1] This results in giving a too static metaphysics of being a much greater dynamism. The idea of form is no longer that of a lifeless statue, but becomes the integrating principle of structure in process. The accent is on relation and union, love, all essential factors of being. It only remains to harmonize the Teilhardian concept of energy with the metaphysics of created being and the communion of saints.

We cannot very well deny the feat of the ape who joins two bamboo sticks together to make himself a tool, or saves up slugs and exchanges them with his mates (though we need give no symbolic meaning to it, since it is only a question of tools). Instinctive behavior affords surprising evidences of the aesthetic in animals—the birds of paradise which not only perform complicated dances, but build bowers and decorate them with colored or shining objects, even going as far as painting them with crushed berries.[1] Acknowledgement of the brute's full powers does not require us to deny that the dimension of the human psychism is of another order, or that animal perception of forms does not run on the abstract lines of the concept of a triangle. To see in the complexity of the human brain and its capacity for speech, or, even prior to speech, the abstractive powers which speech develops, is a matter of actual experience—which, in a Thomistic context, in no way leads to materialism, since the complexly organized human brain and the more complex human soul are two counterbalanced affirmations, with this qualification, that, as metaphysics shows, the soul is much more than the brain, yet powerless to operate in this life otherwise than in cerebral conditions. The materialist by-passes facts and says that the psychic is *merely* the cerebral. The Thomistic realist simply says that, in this life, every psychic act is a cerebral act whose neurophysiological aspect must not make us forget the complementary and inseparable psychological aspect which the psychologist encounters and the metaphysician explains.

[1] This is an activity which, though instinctive, is nonetheless evidence of an elementary awareness and pursuit of beauty far superior to automatisms as complex as the dance-language of bees, or the training of fleas and the mushroom-culture among ants.

Scientific phenomenology takes its stand at the level of the immanent, which has its own special inner coherence. At this level, it verifies *emergence*. That is to say, the spiritual, ever immanent in the unity of being, complies more and more with some guiding force, and that the emergence of the whole, in relation to its parts, already denotes some degree of transcendence. But only metaphysics can give us the transcendent in its complete splendor at both the human and the divine levels, and explain the whole meaning of integration as the principle of new forms.

We see, then, that, if scientific phenomenology is the daughter of the synthesis of the sciences, this synthesis will be incomplete without the added union of this phenomenology and metaphysics. Though it is incomplete as far as an over-all grasp is concerned, the coherence at the level of the immanent and its emergence is enough to establish certain *common values* which allow for agreement on the necessity and the value of the human task. It leads as well to an apologetic.

The human mind likes simple ideas. There are apparent contradictions in reality which arise from incomplete knowledge and the diversity of viewpoints—contradictions which Aristotle, like Hegel and Marx, clearly pointed out. And men are disposed to get rid of these contradictions by denying certain aspects of reality. Truth lies in an *integrating, interpretive synthesis of these seeming contradictions*. Thomism, more than any other philosophy, seems to have achieved this realist synthesis. It has succeeded in this because it has understood that to distinguish two things is not to separate them, that to affirm a perfection is not to deny its humble roots. It has succeeded because it is a philosophy of analogy, that is, it is a synthesis of the like and the unlike. In Thomism, the pseudo-problems of the relations between soul and body, brute and man, nature and supernature, grace and free will, the immanent and the transcendent, disappear. The human soul is only a degree above the brute soul, but this is enough to result in total difference in the metaphysical order. Nature is not opposed to supernature. And supernature is not just a superadded glorification of nature. It is a new degree of that creative Presence which gives nature its being. This new degree, the principle of which is the love of God freely given, cannot be completely manifest until nature reaches the stage of man, a spiritual being capable of freedom and responsibility and in personal rapport with God.

We see, then, how scientific phenomenology cannot reach its full stature outside union with a philosophical cosmology. Further development of the former renders solid metaphysical inquiry more necessary than ever. Modern science demands greater precision in metaphysics; certain foreign elements in its ideas of the soul and of God can no longer be tolerated. But let us never forget that the coalescence of viewpoints on being, and the fact that God's heaven is to be perceived in the contexture of this earth, must not make us overlook the distinction between them. Science looks at the scientific aspect and that alone, and metaphysics at the metaphysical aspect; each sees a distinct aspect of one, single reality. Nothing, for example, would be more wrong than to make of Teilhard's within of things a metaphysical concept, when it is a scientific notion. Yet the "within of things" and Thomistic "form" are not independent of one another. The within, observable by science in the organic integration at the level of the composite, though organically explainable through integration, is metaphysically explainable by the formal organizing principle. So, too, if cybernetics provides us today with a mathematical theory of information, we must not conclude that it gives us a new Thomism. Rather, this information, a measurable scientific concept, is an aspect of the integrated composite, peculiarly suited to the philosophical notion of form.

Now more than ever, scientific phenomenology is demanding a Thomistic renovation in fidelity to the principles—not the terminology—of St. Thomas. It is to be wondered whether Thomists will be able to catch up with life again in the work of the world's salvation.

VI

Teilhardian Realism, the Problem of Evil, and Christian Hope

THE problem of the relationship between science and philosophy, between materialism and spiritualism, does not exhaust the objections caused by misunderstanding Teilhard. The protests of his adversaries come of their belief that he completely distorts Christian thought. For them, the Teilhardian conception is a negation of freedom and grace—everything happens by natural determinisms. God, in chains to his forced labor, loses all freedom and initiative. His very Incarnation is commanded by evolution without any question of pardon or redemption. Man is free only to bow to the lucky automatisms of history, which, despite some possibility of failure, set us forcibly on our way toward the perfect society of the noösphere, which God will only have to glorify in order to come and dwell therein at the end of time. Teilhard's system, we are told, is the negation of morality. Let history take its course, we have no responsibility in it. And that steady ascent of the spiritualizing process in nature appears opposed to the idea of the rupture caused by the first fall. It is true that God created, in nature and supernature, a quasi-perfect man destined to happiness, but in the disobedience of original sin, man smashed that natural goodness, at the same time becoming deprived of his

149

preternatural gifts and corrupting all nature. The world is thus hopelessly lost, and only God's free initiative in redemption can save it. Sin means redemption, means the cross. But Teilhard's world, his critics say, is an easy, optimist world, whereas the Christian world is a world of asceticism, sacrifice, and the cross. The Christian chastises his sinful flesh and shuts himself off from the world, that valley of tears, that land of exile and kingdom of Satan. As for human freedom, it is not especially a capacity for good. It appears more often to be a choice of evil, making the world inhuman, absurd, diabolical. For anyone contemplating the world of our atomic era, the picture is neither pretty nor hopeful. Should one not be inclined, then, to think that man is on the point of botching creation (which God will apocalyptically reestablish), and not that we are headed for a peaceful noösphere? Teilhard, with his confidence in human nature, in man as created and redeemed, would doubtless reply that, after all, we are only at the beginning of evolution; that we are as yet too close to Pithecanthropus; that, though responsible beings, we are still very ignorant of good and evil and are like witless, mischievous, ignorant children.

It is, then, a question of discovering whether—yes or no—Teilhard's world is a world of freedom; whether—yes or no—his world is a sinful, fallen world in need of a Savior. Everything we have so far seen provides the answer: Teilhard's world is the natural aspect—therefore a wittingly incomplete view—of the Christian world. Its only interest is to bring us to accept the truth of Christianity. So, far from opposing it, we should rather try to profit from Teilhard's point of view, and strive to resolve any apparent contradictions.

150

Human Freedom and Natural Morality

That it should be necessary to defend the Teilhardian conception of *freedom* shows how difficult it is to understand it, for freedom is at the heart of Teilhardian thought. What distinguishes the human level for Teilhard—and the neurophysiologist confirms this—is the appearance of a freedom that increases with culture. The acquisition of perfect freedom—this is the meaning of history. And not an absurd freedom such as Gide's or Sartre's, or an enslaved freedom such as the Marxists', but true, human freedom, *personal adherence*[1] to that good which is not egotistic, but communal. In evolution, there are various automatisms, some of which work progressively toward freedom, and others regressively against it. In stating his facts, Teilhard shows that, all in all, it is the positive automatisms entailing freedom which count. In spite of the horrors of the modern world, its wars, its oppressed or starving peoples, the world is, in general, culturally and humanly ahead of former civilizations. We use our material and technical resources badly, but we do have them, whereas our ancestors, with the best intentions, could not have improved over us very much, except at the level of solidarity in human misery. And so it is quite true that there is a current of human thought and invention, of need for justice and humanity, which presses ahead in progress, though this progress is retarded by all sorts of catastrophes, ignorance, and contradictory factors of consequence enough to make us doubt it and to turn the world into a hell. In Teilhard's eyes, the chief characteristic of the modern

[1] St. Paul's law of the heart. So, too, evolution imposes nothing on God and sets no limits to his freedom, for it is his own mighty plan.

world, as it begins its unification, is that, due to progress, human freedom is now in a position to assume greater power than ever. It is now man's privilege to take evolution deliberately into his own control. And either he will opt for the good, for the normal meaning of history, as willed by God, and work to make a happier world disencumbered of its evil automatisms to the degree that he can and will; or he will refuse. He has the power to cause a further increase of evil, to cause, perhaps, even evolution to fail, though in Teilhard's eyes this is, in spite of everything, improbable. Man's power tends, rather, to inhibit and disorganize, for goodness is so rational a force that it always imposes itself, at least a little, on our freedom. Teilhard is neither Pelagian nor Manichaean, and in his eyes freedom does not contradict grace. His thought is so far from being opposed to morality that it may be taken as a *normative phenomenology,* a *deontology of nature* which defines what we must do to carry out the human task toward the full flowering of evolution and history. For the benefit of those who believe in the absurd and deny value, it shows the work being done on earth, how it is our privilege to take it, freely, in hand and humanize it, and how a refusal will lead necessarily to our destruction. For Marxists, who see this task but minimize personal freedom, it shows that nothing can be done without the development of this freedom, which is of our very nature. Without this freedom, there can be no possibility of progress. In the face of the enormous growth of man's technical power over the earth and himself, there is an absolute need for the union of all men, believers and non-believers, around *common values.* Teilhard gives us the possibility of a *natural morality of human values* grounded on solid, objective, scientific arguments.

In place of the traditional apologetic which starts from God in order to arrive at morality, Teilhard puts morality as a preliminary, and shows that its logical justification is belief in God. Nor is this natural morality of his at all a situation-ethic. It is a morality rooted in the essence of human nature, in the human task as willed by God, who has committed to us the work of perfecting creation, of finding the right answer to every situation, and this not as an imperative, but as a reasonable *indication* which we ought to accept. It is a morality of engagement in the world, but only in order to build a genuinely human world, and to strive toward the expulsion of evil. It is a morality of the full flowering of the complete man, the man of flesh, and ordered to the full development of his free will in the service of good. It is a morality of human nature, but not a naturalist morality, for human nature, at the level of action, is above all revealed in its capacity for self-control and judgment—the art of using its brain humanly in every area of true love. Human biology no longer means the triumph of human force, racism, Kinsey's classifications, or Freud's instincts. It means using the human brain in a human way in order to accept one's human condition and to discover what is *normal,* what conforms to our psychobiological nature, and what is abnormal, contrary to that nature. Here again, Teilhard has only pointed out, without elaborating it, this whole normative aspect, but no one has sufficiently understood that *The Divine Milieu,* his major work, is not that of a mediocre Christian mystic. Once more, it is the work of a scientist who knows the phenomenon of man. Hence, its agreement with the traditions of the moralists is not due to his own moral convictions, but to the coalescence of conclusions from science and faith.

In this natural morality, Teilhard is utterly and genuinely Catholic in the line of descent, as Maritain so well shows, from St. Thomas, who defines morality in terms of what is natural. Catholicism has never professed the Protestant pessimism which sees the Fall as having obliterated all natural capacity for good which does not come of the quasi-miraculous grace of God.

Teilhard stresses the value of human effort and the human task. It seems to him more constructive to depict this *positive* aspect of the way of working out one's salvation in action that is meditated on, thought out and prayed over, than to devote attention to the classical enunciations of that whole *pathology of free behavior* which is sin. About this he has nothing new to say, in this respect differing from the neurophysiologist,[1] although he has, along the axis of evolution, the right to define the moral aspect of a humanizing meaning of history, not as submission to history, which is the Marxist error, but as a will to create human history freely and collectively, and thereby *give* history its meaning.

However, Teilhard has never implied that the human task was easy, and he did not call for a terrific effort of mind and will. He knew frustration, and his hope is not a complacent optimism, but the *Christian virtue of trust*. He knows that nothing is possible without God's grace, which, so far from interfering with our freedom, enlightens and sustains it. He understands the power of the sacraments. We find him putting on paper words conveying world-dread and nausea which resemble Sartre's outbursts, but he was only taking his bearings; he was far from

[1] Neurosis is a pathological breakdown of cerebral functions alienating freedom, whereas sin leads to freely bringing about such a breakdown.

believing that they pointed to the absurdity of the world. He knew that his own imperfection, his own incompleteness, his own deviations, things against which all of us must struggle with all our might,[1] were also involved. The "divine milieu" lays heavy emphasis on the values of diminishment—asceticism, mortification, suffering, old age, death. It is too often thought that this is Teilhard's only concession to traditional spirituality. But in a biologist's eyes, these diminishment factors are an essential constituent in human nature, though this does not make them more pleasant. There has been an over-cultivation of the idea that the ascetical virtues are a struggle against nature, nearly a de-personalizing process. In reality, they are necessary for a true unfolding of our nature and our personality. Anyone who seeks unlimited self-expansion will collapse into a power-neurosis, into the sin of egotism and pride, and therefore be incapable of a balanced personality. Man, as a limited being, needs to feel his limitations, to understand himself in his weakness and suffering and mortality; he must not make himself God. Though it is true that sanctity surpasses wisdom and can go counter to it without forgetting the virtue of prudence, and though it is not necessary to be wise and well-balanced in order to be a saint, yet it remains that there is a standard common to wisdom and sanctity, and that everyday sanctity—this side of utter heroism— is very often the criterion, the road, of wisdom, that wisdom

[1] We cannot deny the cruelty and the hideousness in life, but we must not be dismayed. Yet, we have to learn that the world is not God, that the great law of evolutionary progress rests on the dissipation of energy. The less is the foundation of the more. The factors of diminishment are necessary to the ascent. It is a tragic law, but it makes man and the Incarnation possible.

which is *complete health,* the fine balance of an organism made of spirit and matter.

So let us cease accusing Teilhard of denying human freedom, of ignoring sin and the self-control which helps us to avoid it. Nor must we think that he said everything there was to be said about it. We can only supplement the directives of traditional morality with the wise observations he drew from the main axis of the phenomenology of evolution.

World-Weakness and Human Sin

There remains the important question of original sin and evil in Teilhard's doctrine. Here again, his duty is to emphasize certain less traditional, natural aspects, prescinding, without considering as nul, from others of which he says nothing, since they do not enter in the axis of his thought. Every Christian knows that evil comes of original sin as cause of the Fall and of actual sin, both inspired by the devil, and therefore realities which pertain especially to the supernatural life and our relations with God. In no way concerned with this specific aspect, as a scientist, Teilhard has only the duty to show us the natural aspect of evil, to show us its role in the nature of the world, and how its characteristics, as peculiar to human sin, are, despite their supernatural significance, also a consequence of the incompleteness and weakness of created being—which, in this respect, already seems to require some sort of redemption.

It is important, therefore, that he reveal those natural aspects of evil, as perceived especially in the phenomenology of evolution, which, regardless of what is said to the contrary, lend evil and creation a tragic greatness. Theologians have long pointed out an aspect of evil inherent in created being: a *lack of being* stemming from the fact that a creature, not being God, cannot be perfect. Teilhard resumes this argument of the *incomplete world,* and develops from it the chronological aspect of the *world as unfinished.* He adds to this the dialectical perspective of the *evil of maturation,* the evil in birth-process, the failures, abortions, frustrations. The long road of evolution is like a Calvary, marked out by creatures who have suffered and fallen along the way. The determinisms of creation are factors which make necessary all the waste, the mighty squandering of energy so that man might be. This process continues in human history, but now a new factor appears—human freedom. The evolutionary failures and abortions of a world in process have given place to human dissonances, which very often are not sins: ignorance, error, folly, heedlessness of the consequence of human acts and human duty—countless determinisms restricting judgment and freedom. To this there is added real sin or some part of real sin in all action. Human progress, therefore, has been continually retarded, and the world has become more imperfect, absurd, and in contradiction to God's will. Evil thus appears, from a natural point of view, far more widespread than man's sin. It consists primarily in *the weakness of the imperfect.* Teilhardian realism is hence able to see the truth contained in a pessimism which condemns everything that goes bad in the world, yet it can also see it as a necessary consequence of that plan which God has freely willed: the attainment to the level of free man, starting from a complexifying evolution. While sin itself is a proof of our possession of the greatness of a spiritual creature, it is primarily an indication of our weakness. Human sin has always been possible, because from the very first man has had the dimension of freedom. Yet, it is certain that the more aware we become of our determinisms, the more responsible we are. Progress in medicine and psychology in their investigations of morbid determinisms will, far from abolishing sin, only make sin more possible, and, in increasing freedom, make it less excusable. And so this increase in freedom requires a corresponding increase in consciousness of good and evil, of the normal and the pathological. The more we progress, the more culpable our ignorance and want of due reflection become. We must feel ourselves ever more responsible before God in the degree that our knowledge and power advance, and in the degree that we understand that evil in all its aspects can be forced back. This is part of the human task and of the aim of creation.

Human progress drives evil back, be it pathological evil or the evil of sin, and enlightens us about the nature of good and evil. But Teilhard, of course, never fell into the utopian, Marxist idea of an earthly paradise in which the vanishing of all disorder and a stoical acceptance of death will bring the reign of perfect happiness. Sin is inherent in human nature, it is a counterpart of human freedom. Moral obligation does not rest on any external, rational ground, religious or psychobiological. Even a man who understands what evil is will always be free to choose to abandon himself to it. To choose good, to be normal, demands an interior adherence, a painful asceticism of the will for which sensible training can help to make us better prepared, but which will always require an effort that one can and should be able to refuse. Man must remain free in the way God made him. Here, then, is a natural view of various aspects of evil to which we can —indeed, we must—join the supernatural aspect, the real, human-divine dimension, of man's responsibility before God,[1] Who wills the success of the individual and of all creation, as well as of the grace given to help us, and the devil who comes to tempt us. Teilhard believes with the Church that evil has this particular dimension. We saw how, both in the natural and supernatural design of evolutive creation, the Incarnation takes its place as a kind of justification of suffering in evolution. It is a justification guaranteeing the value of the work in which God shares as a model for men and a revelation of the love of God, the God-Man, Who, as Head and motive-force of the Mystical Body, the universal Christ, will carry history in Christic terms to its Omega. There is question here of an overlooked natural aspect, and it must not be distorted by separating it from the traditional teaching of the Church which reveals the full meaning of the Incarnation: the reëstablishment of a supernatural order which is inserted in the natural.

Original Sin and the Fall

There is in all of this one very important thing which Teilhard wishes to point out without any intention of abolishing the theology of the Fall, the redemption, the salvific character of the Incarnation, or the necessity of the cross. Yet, we might ask, must this aspect necessarily be presented as a history in the supernatural order distinct from and opposed to a profane his-

---

[1] This is primarily, now and forever, a natural responsibility of man toward himself and the human race.

tory? Is there really any necessary opposition between a history of indefinite natural progress toward a happy fulfillment of human nature and the theory of the Fall and of the redemption, that is, of an irreparable rupture through man's fault? We saw how Teilhardian realism recognizes the significant place of evil and human sin, and how, in its view, the world progresses despite the evil and sin which retard progress. Christ and the Church thus exist to put man back on the right road, and this is the meaning of the redemption. On the other hand, there is a certain traditional view which cannot thus stress the Fall consequent on sin without confusing the supernatural order in which the break with God occurred, and the far less seriously disrupted natural order; and without also grossly exaggerating, from the viewpoint of strictly human culture, the conditions of original justice. But, of course, we can question the legitimacy of such exaggeration. Long ago, St. Irenaeus pointed out that Adam's sin could have been the sin of a child! We dwell too much on the idea that original sin is proof of man's superiority, whereas sin is a sign of inadequacy and weakness. From the very first, man has been enough man to be capable of sin and responsibility. But this evidence of freedom, lacking in animals, does not necessarily lead to the conclusion that his condition was other than the savagery and absence of culture which science indicates. What is the sin of pride but the sin of the weak who believe themselves to be strong, to be like God—the temptation of a man who, having escaped from a condition of animality, comes into an intuitive religious awareness and is tempted to preëmpt almightiness and go counter to his moral sense? Man did not alienate himself by attributing his own powers to God, as Marxism says. The alienation came of his attributing to himself God's omnipotence, contradicting his natural limits. It matters little precisely what the first sin was. The Fall had only minor importance on the natural level of the phenomenology of evolution. It did not much alter the actual cultural and technical acquisitions of man, though it diminished his self-control and, therefore, the right human use of those acquisitions. The thing which changed completely was the supernatural aspect of man's relationship with God, and it is on that level, under that aspect—utterly beyond the purview of science—that the Fall and the redemption have their place. If suffering and death made their appearance, and if those sometimes exaggerated preternatural gifts were lost, this does not mean that suffering and death are not written into the very psychobiological nature of man.[1] Pain in particular takes other forms than that which the nerves provide as a natural protection. There is pain in the uneasiness and anxiety, for instance, which is the real pain of childbirth, a pain which is not the effect of the actual delivery, but of a sort of conditioning, perhaps even of neurotic aggravation, of the physical pain. These are natural aspects of suffering which may have a connection with sin without the latter being the cause of the suffering itself. It is not nature that has changed because of the break with God, but the ability to deal with it and make it develop in a balanced, peaceful way. That the first sin had hereditary consequences shocks us because we envisage it at the natural level of the chromosomes. But it is really a matter of a new state of affairs between man and God, and there all the arguments of the theologians are

[1] We must not forget that the preternatural gifts are a modification of that nature.

161

valid. Our separated conditions endures, and only God's initiative can restore the bridge between the human race and Him.

In the realm of paleontology, the problem which original sin raises about the first man, or the first men, is a pseudo-problem. Indeed, science will never have an answer for it. As Teilhard says in a much misunderstood passage, paleontology is ignorant of man's beginnings. It first encounters his species only when it is sufficiently rich in individuals. However, the fact that most paleontologists, Teilhard included, are favorable to *monophyletism*—the theory of the unique origin in time and space of the human stock—is in harmony with the *monogenism* insisted on, at least for the moment, by the Church.

Whether or not there was a zero instant before the act of creation, the world is dependent on God. The Church requires us to believe in the beginning of creation, but it does not admit of the proposition that a world of indefinite duration in the past was not created. Likewise, while the Church does not admit polygenism, on the ground that it threatens the dogma of original sin (see *Humani Generis*), it nonetheless does allow private, prudent, free inquiry into the question.

In reality, the scientific conception of the world, which defines man in terms of his freedom, sees original sin as certain, for experience demonstrates that in this weak, fragile creature, freedom has consisted in doing evil without freedom destroying responsibility. It would be vain, though we used arguments from every field of knowledge, to try to show man the advantages and the reasonableness of goodness, which is the sole guarantee of balance and of individual and social progress. Man will always seem to show an irrational, pathological preference for evil and disorder, and this betokens an almost second nature, a sign at the same time of those two in no way contradictory aspects of his original weakness as proved by science and of his original deviation as declared by faith. It is all an aspect, a consequence of his original weakness, of special significance both from the supernatural viewpoint and from that of the control of nature, without anything in it radically altering the meaning of history.

The Christian Endeavor

Teilhard's scientific realism is neither an optimism nor a pessimism. It falls neither into Pelagianism, which attributes all to man, nor into Manichaeism, which says that man is lost. It does not separate man from his creator, yet sees our lost world nonetheless as a created world and, what is more, a redeemed world in both the orthodox and natural senses of the word, a world through which flow grace and the Holy Spirit and the assistance of angels, but a world, too, where Satan reigns. Teilhard is convinced of the final happy issue, because it conforms to evolution, sin notwithstanding. But this is on condition that enough responsible men accept adequate involvement in the right direction. Teilhard, in showing us the meaning of history and helping to put us on the right road and to muster mankind's forces for the construction of the future, is not prepared to predict positively whether this will happen. He only believes that it will happen. Here, where Satan himself must bow to the divine will, man with his freedom retains the power to arrest the evolutive process of which he is the final unfolding.

Teilhard indicates how man must devote himself to continuing this process, whose special energies he has worked out in terms of that energy of centration, as an aspect of love, which, in order to be manifested—because of the principles of thermodynamics—requires the dispersion of ordinary energy, thereby increasing entropy. A whole *spiritual thermodynamics* of moral values is proposed for our freedom. We must work for the increase of love as the instrument of ascent and coherence. We must also take care not to squander the energy of the world, but to put it to the maximum use of the ascent. Again, this requires painful asceticism. Teilhard has never said that the unification of the world was a univocal process, or that there was no threat of a new totalitarianism. He made an heroic attempt to define the noösphere and to educe its principles, but his work needs the personal effort of others. If we do not take care, it will be the multiple, the divergent, the depersonalizing, under the appearances of unity and convergence, which will come to pass.

Teilhard's teaching is a call to *personal effort,* not a submission to happy automatisms. The meaning of history is neither prophecy nor slavery; it is *duty.* Here, indeed, there is adherence to the teaching on original sin and the Fall, but with no despondent resignation, or any thought that in our lost world there is nothing we can do. This do-nothing excuse, on the ground that all action is doubtful and runs the risk of missing perfection, is by no means a Christian attitude. True, man is inclined to sin; true, he is weak and needs God's rescue and help; true, he has been saved. But Christ's redeeming role must not make us passive. In saving us, Christ taught us to save ourselves, to work out our own salvation. The cross which reëstablished our relationship with God is not a magic means which saved us in spite of ourselves.

We are not the oppressed citizens of a totalitarian society which drives us willy-nilly toward goodness. We are active members of the Mystical Body whose Head leaves it to our free coöperation to realize the Terrestrial City by the help of his grace. To act, we must hope and believe that success is possible in the face of the known hardships of the task. Teilhard helps us here by showing us success in the natural order, but a natural order which is not to be separated from the supernatural, from God's hidden presence. We know, of course, that God will have the last word, but what an infinite pity if it therefore be said that God must take the credit for a job which should have been properly our own, and which our incompetence will have caused to miscarry!

VII

The Resacralization of the Profane World

The Profane and the Sacred

It has been a long time since the human race, still in its infancy, ignorant, susceptible to the marvellous, easily astonished and terrified, saw the whole world as full of mystery, inexplicable, peopled with gods, spirits, jinns, and demons, a world in which magic was a must for life. Nothing in that world was profane, nothing was secular. Everything was sacred. We do not, of course, lament the passing of that time of fear and terror. Yet, our own scientific and technical times, in which everything has been explained or can be explained, when science seems to have have reduced religion to pointlessness, where everything has become profane and secular—is it not the return of a time of fear, of terror and anxiety, faced as it is with the appalling forces of human technical knowledge which nothing seems able to hold to the service of mankind? No talisman, no magic can protect us against the insanity of the technocrats, nothing except a return to a concept of the *genuinely sacred*.

Those early men were right. They were expressing their human quality to the full in affirming the *existence of the sacred,* in seeing something sacred, some mystery in everything. Their only mistake, in their ignorance, was not to know what the character of the sacred consists in, that it is not just a ready remedy making up for a lack of knowledge, not an external quickening of things by spirits.

At the birth of the modern mind, we see a twofold current. There is, first of all, stemming from Greek thought which stripped away all the magic, the growth of *rational, scientific thinking* which helps us understand the world and gives us control of it, but which offers us, in place of the old, unknowable mysteries, an unknown *"peau de chagrin"* which steadily contracts without ever ceasing to be infinite. Thus, a profane, secular thought becomes mistress of a realm which tends to expand over all reality, all practical, useful, concrete aims in life, and we end with a world in which there are only engineers of things and of souls in a world of mathematics and statistics. Soon men may be governed by automatic machines, that is, alas, by the blunders of those who built them.

Secondly, there is the influence of a *refining process of religious feeling,* which led to recognition of the true, spiritual God, thanks to the slow maturation of the people chosen to defend monotheism against idols—the people of Abraham and Moses, who in due time witnessed Christ's Incarnation and the establishment of the Christian Church. The realm of the genuinely sacred was thus preserved. This sacred in the thought of the Jewish people and of St. Paul was not separated from the profane realm. The divisions created by Platonism and Gnosticism had no influence here as yet. The recognition of God's greatness in comparison to idols did not result in separating Him from His

167

work. God was in fire, He was in the wind, He was in the desert and in the stars, He spoke to the shepherds (Loew).

The critical act in the drama of the modern world was the separation of science and faith, begun in the Middle Ages with the first blows of rationalism and mysticism, and it exploded with Galileo. Descartes and Pascal, the philosophy of the eighteenth century, and the positivism and scientism of the nineteenth bear witness to it. The growth of scientific and technical knowledge appeared to come only at the cost of a withdrawal from faith. The truths of Christianity were compared to pagan legends. In a scientifically explained world, there is no room for God as creator, except perhaps in the privacy of the heart of a man who enjoys praying. But so tolerant is secular, profane society that it is willing to let rise the walls of churches, where the sacred is *shut in,* and the cathedral steeples pointing to a celestial *beyond,* where God sits—a beyond which science cannot locate!

This profane, secular attempt of the human mind to comprehend and possess the world is perfectly lawful, as is the recognition of a level of values where the direct intervention of religion is not called for; lawful, too, the rejection of the type of clericalism which would put the priest in the scientist's place. Quite legitimate, also, is that refined religious sense which makes us understand ever more fully the spiritual nature, the greatness of a God Who is *absolutely other,* the *nada* of the mystical dark night. Indeed, it is not only legitimate, it is absolutely necessary to make distinctions, to avoid confusions, but, in Maritain's phrase, *we must distinguish in order to unite.* The wrong thing is to separate, to isolate, to cut off God as residing elsewhere than in a world which can, then, only be known and explained in terms of science.

The profane, the secular, the scientific, the technical must be seen as but one aspect of the world, the other aspect of which is the religious, sacred one. Man is not separate from a nature which he must subdue by doing violence to it. He forms a part of that nature, though he submits to its control, and he must decipher its secret meaning.

Driven into a world outside the profane, the Church attempts the struggle to limit this profane so as to avoid the totalitarianism of the technician and thus preserve essential values. She has given up the direction of the profane, which is a secular business. But she could wish that the technicians were Christians, that the men of the factory and the laboratory were not so forgetful of the oratory; that the specialists in the material realm would remember the spiritual realm; and that the ascendancy of the world and the flesh not make for forgetfulness of the things not of this world. Catholic action and apologetic seem to be trying to reintroduce God by force into a world where He has no place, and hence their annoying, disappointing character. The scientific world does not want God, for it feels no need of Him.

The solution, then, is a return to biblical tradition, that of God as creator, in a denial of Platonism and Cartesianism, in a discovery that the absolutely other is not the absolutely remote, but that its transcendence is revealed in its immanence. God is the absolutely near for the man who knows how to see into the depths of a diaphanous universe. God hides "in the heart of matter." We must present God to this profane world of science and technics in terms of its own language, in the discovery, as yet imperfectly understood by Catholic action, of His presence in the milieu. We must not force attention *elsewhere,* to what is of no interest. Instead, we must compel a clearer vision of the *object* of the technician's efforts, so that his work will be the more thoroughly performed. This is to work with the sacred, with the other side of the profane. It is not something other. It is only another aspect of things, their secret, underlying aspect, the thing that gives them their value. The modern world is not interested in a world-soul, in some non-existent God of pantheism, but neither does it want anything to do with the transcendent God taken as the explanation and mover of the world. What it requires is the certain knowledge that this transcendent God is hidden in immanence, that personal love is the secret of the world. Science will take the road to the oratory, those *more* sacred places and times whose roots are in its own heart, only when it understands that what matters is a yet profounder communion with its own work of technical organization.

Here is the real meaning of Teilhard's work and of the development of the introspective phenomenology which aims at finding the secret of the world at the heart of the world, in an immanence revealing itself as transcendent. *It is a matter of resacralizing a profane world by giving even the profane its own sacred character.* Hence, the importance of a thorough understanding of Teilhard if his message is to bear fruit.

Modern science has been, in great part, responsible for the desacralization of the world, philosophers and theologians being unable to grasp its real significance. But even so, by an inevitable, natural process, the progress of analytical science, which tore down and then remodelled nature, leads it on to spiritual values.

We cannot let it conclude from there to an over-all materialism. Instead, faithful to the mind of St. Thomas and St. Augustine, we must come to understand, and make others understand, that science has possibilities only if it approaches being as created. The recognition of an incarnate aspect of the sacred reënters the area of its research, though even this is not the main goal. For science must not remain purely analytical. Rather, it must aim at understanding the nature of things from its own point of view. *Now, the sacred forms part of that nature.* Long confined to the surface of things, the realm of accidents in the Thomist sense, science now approaches the inner heart of things: being. Going past the diaphanous, it begins to grasp the within of things.

We must distinguish between the profane and the sacred. We must recognize degrees of the sacred. But it is wrong to separate the two. Everything has its profane aspect and its sacred aspect. The sacred was once a kind of transcendental magic which did violence to things. Today, we see its real nature, which is to give life from within through immanence, to be a constituent part of things, yet without ceasing to be transcendent. The sacred can thus become, at least in part, accessible to the non-believer. We know that Rostand, meditating on man's technical ascendancy, said, although he was not a believer, that every man should be to every other man *a holy thing* commanding reverence.

There was a time, and it has not yet entirely passed, when certain Catholics, mixing one thing with another, believed that prayer and resignation were sufficient for the solution of social problems. Today, when the autonomy of technics and politics is becoming recognized, we see the outline of the error in believing that this autonomy abolishes any interdependence with the religious order. To be a Christian politician does not require contempt for technical solutions, but neither does it involve worshipping them. It does involve giving first place in the quest for such solutions to reverence for the human person.

It is time, then, to stop accusing Teilhard of confusing orders of being, the technical with the religious. It should be understood that he brings to our world, oscillating between distinction of values and their separation, the correct conception of the interdependence of orders, of the variety in viewpoints of one, single object.

What reason is there for thinking that the sacred is better protected the more we separate and confine it, when the protection of its specific nature consists precisely in its very mysteriousness—utterly intimate, hidden and profound—the mysteriousness of a world that has been, seemingly, completely explained? How can we believe that God is more intimately present in our hearts than we ourselves are, if we do not see that that presence is related to the principle of evolving creation, and to the fact that matter is not opposed to spirit, but is involved in a dialectical action of complexification whose term, infinitely transcending natural powers, is the Incarnation of creative love? How can we believe in Christ, if we are not sure that man, the very peak of evolution, so weak, so fragile, and so sinful, yet free and responsible, needed to feel himself helped, strengthened, *saved* by a man, inserted like himself in history, but Whose human nature deserved to be associated in a mysterious union with the divine nature so as to create a new bond between God and man, stronger even than the bond of creation or the intimacy before the Fall?

Created matter, which Love has taken in its arms, this lowly matter from which man's body is made—how can we deny its sacredness when we know that it was one day to be the very pillar of the Incarnation, and that, endlessly, on all the altars of the world, the matter of bread and wine becomes the matter of God's body and blood? The scientific phenomenology of Teilhard, a Catholic priest, ends in that *eucharistic mystery* which made the experience of the true reality under the unchanged accidents so familiar to him. This mystery makes, in a way, for a sort of healthy "materialist" side to Catholicism. It was Christ Who said that spiritual nourishment must use the material means of nourishment. Teilhard gives us a phenomenology of the real presence, the real presence of God in the world, which, though not to the same degree or of the same nature as the eucharistic Presence, is all the same a presence. Everyone knows of Teilhard's wonderful meditation, *Hymn of the Universe,* written when he was in the Mongolian Desert without bread or wine, and how he, as it were, consecrated the world and all human activity to God.

We know Teilhard's devotion to the Sacred Heart, the organic symbol, by God's will, of the love to which he gives its full, cosmic dimension.

The day when, in their faith in the true God, all believers grasp that everything is sacred, that nature is sacred, that all action is sacred, that everyone of their movements is sacred and involves their whole being and the future of the world, a future at once profane and religious—all these are only one thing—on that day, many things will change in the faith they have been reserving only for certain times and occasions. And they will be able to make the meaning of the sacred in things so objectively evident

173

that total faith will not be necessary in order to come to certitude about the common task and common values. Reverence for things and reverence for man will lead to their real inner nature, that is, to God.

Teilhard's opponents are correct in insisting on the necessity of carefully distinguishing between orders and degrees of being and God's activity—which, in fact, Teilhard did, but if Teilhard's readers overlook the true meaning of his message, they risk falling into the error of separating what is not separable, and thus furthering the secularization and profanation of the world.

The Sacrament of Brotherhood

In no area has this profanation been more harmful than in that of *social relationship* among men. We proclaim the spirituality of a soul, as separate from body, and this makes it possible to hand over the body to every sort of social injustice. Now, in the social order, there is no such thing as body and economics on the one hand, and soul and the spiritual on the other, with nothing in common between them.[1] When two men are together, they are, in God's sight, two human beings possessed of immortal souls, and they will maintain this balance only in a relationship of equality where there is mutual respect for one another's freedom and initiative such as God has in His relations with the soul. To secure the *assent* of a being who is our equal, even

[1] The thought of one of our most humane and Christian sociologists is rooted in the teaching of St. Thomas (Chénu: *St. Thomas Aquinas*, New York). So also the spirit of *Économie et Humanisme* (Lebret) and of the Action Populaire founded by Father Desbuquois.

though he is socially or culturally inferior, is the only really human way of governing without force or undue influence.

As Simone Weil has so wonderfully written: "Many a controversy between the right and left is reducible to an opposition between the desires of individual caprice and the desires for social restraint; or, more exactly perhaps, between dread of social restraint and dread of individual caprice. Charity and justice are not involved here. Justice has for its object on earth the exercise of the faculty of consent. To guard it religiously wherever it exists, and to try to create the conditions necessary for its existence wherever it is absent, this is to love justice. . . . Freedom is the concrete possibility of giving consent. Men need equality only in relation to that. The spirit of brotherhood consists in wishing it for all men. The possibility of consent is afforded in a life which possesses the motives for consent. Destitution, privations of soul and body hinder the possibility of consent taking place within the hiddenness of the heart. Freedom is the spice of true obedience."

Another example of lamentable profanation, in an area which is a special instance of human social relationship, but in a degree of infinitely greater intimacy because it is the greatest intimacy which can possibly exist between two incarnate creatures, concerns human sexuality. The libertine exalts flesh without soul, which is total profanation. The puritan, in separating the love of the flesh apart, acts just as profanely. Whether one gives full rein to his instincts or shuts them out altogether, there is equal mutilation of man. Modern neurophysiology concurs with the true Catholic morality of the marriage sacrament in reestablishing the truth: that human sexuality is normal and right only

175

when it is a fleshly communion of two beings, body and soul, in God's presence. This involves at the same time flesh and control of the flesh, not by a pure, separate spirit, but control which is also fleshly, since there is question here of a right human use of cerebral functions which are the fundamental principle of personal control and of awareness of another in the full degree of his human personality.

To recognize this sacred character of the world, even though not following it to its ultimate conclusion, means a refusal to be shut up in a technical, quantitative, analytical, and materialist totalitarianism. It means a rejection of the superficial and a projection of one's gaze into the diaphaneity, down into the depths of existence. It means passing beyond the accidental and transitory to a vision of the one in the many, the converging, in the diverging, the ascent hidden under decaying standstill.

In giving back to us, through his scientific vision of the world, the meaning of the sacred, Teilhard not only sets up an apologetic based on the converging harmonies of various views of a single reality, while avoiding the errors of concordism and separatism and helping to bring the modern non-believer, from the latter's own viewpoint, to philosophy and religion. He also establishes a common politics. Or rather, within the freedom of technical, political involvement, he reveals the human *philosophy and morality of politics* which should be the common characteristic of a variety of options. In his criticism of traditional democracy, fascism, and Communism, he shows the necessity of passing beyond these if mankind is to be saved. The *sacralization of politics* does not mean the divinization of a party. It means positing that a political system which aims at the government of human affairs *is by definition a sacred realm,* and that any error in it injurious to man comes as a profanation—an idea which propagandists of anything in the least way evil should ponder on. We should shun having unclean hands as we would having no hands at all, and, without Pharisaical legalism, touch a man only with hands that are as pure as the priest's at the consecration—with a feeling of our own unworthiness. If politics, in fact, choses for its rule "to love one's neighbor as oneself," or the Sermon on the Mount,[1] the road to the noösphere would be open. This does not involve denying the fact of sin. It does involve the need of a little more understanding on the part of politicians of what being human means.

We see here the urgent need of taking our bearings within the meaning of Teilhardian phenomenology, so as to give all men a *scientific culture and humanism* which will not be a caricature or mutilation of humanistic culture, but a scientific confirmation of everything that is certain in traditional humanism.

However, the purpose of this book is not to develop all the consequences of the Teilhardian vision. It is to justify the values and the genuine Catholicism in that vision. We think we have sufficiently shown how Teilhard limits himself to a purely scientific point of view which ultimately converges on philosophical and religious questions. His resacralization of the world through a scientific phenomenology of interiority and diaphaneity brings us to discuss, finally, the relation of Teilhard the scientist to poetry and mysticism.

[1] True greatness comes of true reverence and love. "Blessed are the gentle, for they shall inherit the earth."

177

Scientific Knowledge and Aesthetic Knowledge

To call Teilhard a poet is a certain compliment to his style and thought. A talent for poetry was also to be found in another great Catholic geologist, Pierre Termier.

However, the compliment bears some ambiguity, for it makes Teilhard a poet as opposed to his scientific character. If he is a poet, it is in the realm of the *beautiful* as opposed to the real, the concrete. The poet is a dreamer. We may admire but need not believe in him. He does not belong to the objective, the dimensional, the scientific.

Are we to say, then, that because he is a serious scientist, Teilhard is not a poet, or that his poetry is purely a matter of language and style? By no means. That would be a further betrayal of Teilhard and of more than Teilhard. It would mean missing another fresh synthesis, another humanly valuable convergence, that of the essential harmony which should pertain between science and poetry, science and art, the scientific viewpoint of being and the aesthetic view of being.

We saw that though scientism is correct in affirming that nothing escapes the attention of science, it is wrong to say that the scientific approach is the sole source of certitude, that is, of intimate union with objective truth. Teilhard's superdevelopment of the specific possibilities of science makes more than ever necessary a thorough study of the various branches of knowledge and of philosophical and theological certitude in independent research. Likewise, moral certitude of the good is not a matter of mere subjectivity or feeling. It must rest on objective knowledge of the true and its established norms, on a knowledge in which the specific nature of morality is not something dependent on the directives of a psychobiologist or theologian. The modern world is too inclined to think that certitude and valid inquiry exist only in the scientific field. It takes that word "science" as it is presently used by the natural sciences, and rejects the traditional idea that there is scientific knowledge in the philosophical and theological fields.[1] A comparative study of the techniques used in research and the acquirement of knowledge and certitude in the various fields could be devoted to showing that experimental science has no special privileges, and that it stands on foundations analogous to other systems of knowledge involving experience, reason, and faith. Experimentation is not the private property of the scientist, though experience has its special aspect for him. Reasoning is not the private property of the philosopher, despite the technicality of his reasoning, and believing is not the private property of the theologian, though ordinarily he should have active faith. The three kinds of specialists, in fact, have their own proper methods of experimenting, reasoning, believing, corresponding to their techniques and their points of view.

Along with these areas of scientific, philosophical, and religious or moral knowledge, we must include that of *aesthetic* certitude and knowledge. Art is a means of knowing the world and man. It is not just an amusement. The artist is not a photographer copying the appearances of things. He, too, searches into the diaphanous universe, striving to reveal its soul, and this is the meaning of painting and poetry and music. The artist, too, is an analyst in his handling of the techniques of sound and color, but

[1] Chénu, *Is Theology a Science?*, New York, 1959.

his concern is the *form* resulting from their synthesis, whether it be natural or something he created in his brain. The artist is specifically devoted to expressing the very synthesis, the very totality we have been studying. What is physical beauty but a synthesis of material qualities (e.g., muscular tonus, smoothness of skin) each quite unable, by itself, to convey the specific character of the beauty which exists only in their integration? What is music, which gives us so clear a conception of the spiritually pure, but a synthesis of sounds having its own special form? Every attempt of modern painting or poetry, even in their most exaggerated distortions, is a quasi-experimental effort of the artist the better to express the true reality of the world and man, the surreal, the subconscious. The quest of abstract art for pure, disincarnate form, or a Matisse revealing, after prolonged effort, a face in a single stroke. Just as there is a truth in science, a truth in philosophy, and truths of faith very near to the Truth, so there is aesthetic truth, and the fact that definition of it is hard to come by should not make us overlook the contingency in scientific and philosophical truth—or the fact that, as true as they may be, the truths of faith are a long way from exhausting, from yielding up, all the truth that is God.

Synthesis, then, is not only true or good—it is also beautiful. The artist's purpose is to express[1] this beauty in nature, and as difficult as his work is, he directly intuits beauty and is moved by this mode of the aesthetic in being taken as a whole. The scientist's work and viewpoint are so very different that his results seem in opposition to the aesthetic. To talk about muscular tonus

---

[1] He can also express the disorder of sin. The beauty of nature exists in the real, not in the ideal.

and the cost of cold cream when contemplating the soft skin of a beautiful woman's face is not very poetic! There will always be this sort of analysis, but Teilhard's scientific phenomenology shows that it is not enough. We must move on to synthesis, and from the instant the beautiful exists as a quality of the real, an objective process of restoration, after analysis, must give it back its due place. Intuition and the study of the beautiful are not the purpose of science, but science is capable of grasping an aspect of the beautiful just as it does any aspect of the whole of being. Thus, the total view of science comes back by a long road to blend with the intuitions of the poet and the artist. Termier knew this when he so well described the aesthetic sensibility of the scholar and the beauty in the visions of science.

Here, too, the resacralization of the world should lead to rejection of the too sharp division made between profane art and sacred art. While there are degrees of the sacred, the artist, like the scientist, participates in a holy creation.

In the end, then, to say that Teilhard is a poet simply means recognizing that he succeeded in bringing his work to its ultimate conclusion. It would be interesting to compare him with such cosmic artists as Dante and Claudel.

Evolution and Aesthetics

There is one last point of discussion in the encounter between art and Teilhardian thought, or, more precisely, scientific phenomenology. This phenomenology is a dialectics of creation which stresses the spiritualizing complexification which gives us the norm of genuine progress in biological evolution and human history. In this history, the growth of science has been one of the most spectacular indications of this progress. On the other hand, aesthetics, if taken as a personal pursuit, seems in no way to be a part of collective human progress, except perhaps on the technical level. We have only to think of the paintings at Lascaux and Altamira to be persuaded of this, and it is precisely this magical art which best witnesses to the human character of primitives. In the realm of philosophy, it is rather hard to say whether there is a collective progress in knowledge. It would seem that from the first Greek beginnings, the great, fundamental propositions of materialism, realism, and idealism were already present, and that progress here consisted more especially in the way of presenting them, above all in the efforts of realism to meet the demands made on it when confronted with scientific analysis of the world. We might say there is progress in knowledge to the extent that this knowledge rests on an ever more finely differentiated analysis of sensible reality, of what Teilhard calls the "many." To the extent, however, that knowledge and truth depend on what may be called an "obscure intuition" of the one, the absolute, God, there is no historical progress. These things are simply a matter of varying personal dispositions. Such, at the very most, is the case with art, as with natural religion or religious sentiment, which has no interest in elaborating a theology. It comes down to saying that art is closely related to that common substratum in human nature which has existed from the very first, and which depends on that fine prefrontal integration which is the organic condition for heart and love, whereas science, which connotes language, depends to the maximum on cultural training of the noetic brain of reason. Progress can be deceptive, and it is sure progress only when it is a humanizing process coinciding with a certain essential and inalterable permanence. It is not unsignificant that the area in which communication among men of various cultural levels is the easiest is precisely that of art, music in particular, whether it be jazz or Negro spirituals or the interest of the Orinoco primitive in Mozart.

Scientific Knowledge and Mystical Knowledge

Teilhard's phenomenology, so satisfying rationally, is complete and therefore poetic in that it satisfies the heart, that other, higher form of knowledge which the mathematician Pascal considered opposed to scientific knowledge, which was, in his eyes, as in Descartes', purely quantitative. Because it approaches nearer to poetry than philosophical or theological thought, it is, thus, in harmony with *mystical knowledge*. We have tried to show only in what degree Teilhard was the complete scientist, but there is an area in which his science, though it goes far, is transcended. Teilhard, though so little the philosopher and theologian, is at home in the mystical. Unlike his compatriot Pascal, he was able to harmonize the mystical and the scientific, because his mysticism, although an anterior, independent matter,[1] existed in a further projection of his scientific vision, in a supervision which brought him into the presence of the living reality of God. Followers of scientistic rationalism have clung above all to the opposition between mysticism and science, but their science is a mechanist science unaware of the within of things.

[1] Sharing in the thirst for the Absolute, which rejects the transitory, he yet saw no need to turn from the transitory in order to find the absolute, because he could find it in the depths and very nature of the transitory.

There is, in reality, a profound relationship between scientific experience of the sensible and mystical experience of God. In both cases, there is question of contact with a living reality which requires a like cast of mind very different from the conceptual mind of the philosopher. And so, though such a thing is rare, it is not surprising that in Teilhard, the mystical mind becomes but an extension of the scientific mind into a mysticism that is Christian, traditional, of God the wholly other Who draws the mind on toward the one, toward the future—but the mysticism of a scientist for whom the wholly other is not the wholly apart, but the divine milieu, the reason for things, an energy personal and loving. Like all true mystics, like St. Teresa of Avila or St. John of the Cross, Teilhard loses himself in God only the better to find himself, because his God is God the creator and the Omega Point. Teilhard loved life and his work dearly, and as he grew old he used to ask for the grace, not only to die while receiving Communion, but that his dying be itself a communion with others—a grace which his death on Easter eve, April 10th, 1955, would seem to indicate he was granted.

Conclusion

I hope that in these few pages, I have, as a social biologist having due regard for the authentic values of traditional philosophy, succeeded in witnessing to Teilhard and his scientific phenomenology. Sharing as we do in a materialist, desacralized scientific and technical world which is no longer interested in the spiritual, and which risks leading the human race to destruction, we know in what degree Teilhard can be the salvation of that world by winning it from within to the vision of the true message of science. But, rejected as he was all his life, he will be that salvation only if he is allowed to fulfill his vocation to be a sort of bridge between two worlds really more uncomprehending than hostile. That is what he is—a bridge, if we grasp the fact that he is the complete man of science even when revealing God in the fabric of creation, and the fact that, as the complete thinker, he is in entire agreement with Catholic dogma. Friend and adversary alike have robbed him of his whole *raison d'être*. It is not his aim to be some sort of ill-equipped, incompetent philosopher. His purpose is to be a builder of a spiritualist dialectic of nature consisting of a scientific phenomenology of the within of things, not a metaphysics. In so acting, he does not replace the philosopher, but he does put the philosopher under an obligation to join him in constructing a cosmology which harmonizes both with modern science and with Thomistic metaphysics. On the other hand, he orientates modern man toward philosophy. He keeps, of course, at a distance from philosophy, and we must make a mighty effort if there is to be a *rapprochement* between the two. Yet, buried as he is in the litter of the analysis of being, he restores all being even while saying that his phenomenology is not enough. With human spirituality vindicated by science, there is no longer any reason to reject the teaching of traditional philosophy, since it is impeccably realist. In Teilhard, we attend upon a new St. Thomas faithful to the spirit of the first. But Teilhard's merit consists more in bringing modern man even closer to faith and God than to philosophy and theology. Through his scientific insight, sans concordism, sans confusionism, God's presence is revealed. In its approach to reality from his point of view, science gains access to all reality, therefore to God Himself.

In a world divided against itself, where multiplicity, that is, imperfection, and sin tend to override him, *he is the witness of unity,* of a genuine ecumenism, of coexistence in truth, in charity, those two values of which he testifies that neither can exclude the other because the *secret of truth consists in being animated by love.* Hence, we must reject schism and apartness and the walls which are obstacles between all who, having seized a particle of the truth, falsify it by taking it for the whole. The thing for which Teilhard is most criticized is precisely his refusal to separate God from the world He created, and in which He is present in various degrees according to each creature's nature—prehuman and human, supernatural. Then he has been criticized, not for believing in some sort of nature-goddess, but for recognizing the creative God, lord of all law and chance and human freedom. He has been criticized for refusing to make dissociations in the human task as it works toward the good—as if one could separate what is man's from what is God's, or the role of grace from the role of freedom. How can any man of faith wonder whether men can succeed without God? How does one eliminate God? There is, it is true, a way through one's own free will of eliminating Him, and that is sin. Because Teilhard, who made freedom and responsibility the supreme human value, treated sin as it should be—as a lack or diminution of being—and because he saw no need to treat it otherwise than he did all evidences of weakness or defectiveness in creation, others have concluded that he is a complacent optimist who, without any belief in evil, holds that everything perforce advances steadily from better to better toward the condition of the best of worlds. We would, of course, warn those of Teilhard's readers who may look to him for a kind of complete catechism. Rather, confronting the catechism with Teilhard's thought, we would show how much, in the fresh light he casts, the eternal verities take on an even more incontestable bearing, because the necessary distinctions and formal discontinuities are fitted into a material continuity guaranteeing the meaning of a coherent world in eschatalogical process.

Teilhard comes into his own at a time when the noösphere is finally possible, though it is seriously threatened by individualism and totalitarianism. He comes that all men, having completed an examination of their partial truths, may now become one in the common task of hominization, in which only the most clear-sighted, the most open to the philosophical mind and to grace will see that the building of the City of Man is the more precious and the more sacred because it is a preparation for the City of God.

How interesting and thought-provoking it is that, besides Teilhard, the modern world has another apostle who, unknown in his lifetime like Teilhard, draws it in a special way to God— Father Charles de Foucauld. At first sight, they appear to have little in common. Yet, when countless people feel drawn alike to these two same men, at this same moment of history, it can only mean that the two are closely related. It would be interesting to work out a thorough comparison between the man of world-brotherhood and the man of the noösphere, both devoted to the Sacred Heart. One same vision would embrace the *Hymn of the Universe* offered by the one in the Mongolian Desert, and the prayers of the other in his hermitage at Hoggar. It would then appear how, if they meet in the same Christian mysticism, it is, in both men, a mysticism committed to the service of mankind. Though Foucauld was not a scientist, he was nonetheless fully engaged in the world of science and technics whether as a Moroccan explorer or as a hermit in the Sahara working away, between his prayers, at his Touareg dictionary and grammar. He was a solitary, but today his numerous followers are a living prayer in the heart of the most stricken parts of a de-Christianized world, areas the least able to fight off scientific materialism in its destruction of the old frames of thought. It is impossible that Teilhard de Chardin's ideas should not be just as infinitely important.

If further assurance and explanation be necessary, we may make one final comparison. The scientific world of today has had in Pius XII its very own pope. As moralist and theologian, he tried to help the world of science to see its errors. But he was also ready to bow to genuine advances in science—such as, for example, painless childbirth—regardless of any Marxist context. On the other hand, he maintained a strict respect for scientific autonomy. He did not, for instance, prohibit psychosurgery, as did the Soviet leaders, but only called attention to the dangers in it, leaving the responsibility for particular decisions to the expert's conscience. He ever stressed natural morality, natural law, and the need for coöperation with non-believers in international work in the interests of common values. In Pius XII, mystic and apostle of the communion of saints, the spirit of transcendence was present and made itself heard in a materialist world, though this presence remained, in a way, a little external and limiting. It has never been observed sufficiently how like to Pius Teilhard is in the latter's corroboration of him. In Teilhard, it is not the transcendant which is imposed on the immanent. It is the immanent, that is to say, the inner coherence itself of the vision of science which introduces us to the transcendent and to faith. It is indeed sad that the synthesis of the two points of view has not yet been possible, and it is imperative that it be made soon.

In giving science a truly salvific role by asking it to show man the meaning of his nature and destiny and thus open natural truth to him, Teilhard appears in a singular position in the Church—a position of prophetic choice in a world where science and its Marxist deviations, so attractive to the working class, have such importance. *The Church needs Teilhard's message, and that is why we must see to it that it be rightly understood.*

For this purpose, nothing is more urgent than the reëstablishment of the unity of science and philosophy. No one has said this better than Pius XII in his allocution to the members of the Pontifical Academy of the Sciences, April 24th, 1955:

"Creatures are utterances of truth, which, of their very being, contain no contradition, no confusion, and are always coherent with one another, though often hard to understand because of their profundity, but ever conformable, when clearly understood, to the higher demands of reason. Nature is open to you like a mysterious, but wonderful, book which asks to be perused page by page and correctly read with the care peculiar to the possibility of endless progress. In this way, every step forward continues and corrects the preceding ones and moves steadily upward toward the light of greater comprehension. . . . Science has reached a point where our gaze should easily penetrate the greatest realities and be transformed into one full, harmonious view of all reality. . . .

"When the scientist interprets experimental data and devotes himself to explaining phenomena having material nature as such for their ground, he has need of light which proceeds, inversely, from the absolute to the relative, from the necessary to the contingent, a light capable of showing him that truth which science is not equipped to reach by its own methods, because the totality of that truth escapes the senses. This light is philosophy, that is, the science of the general laws which hold for all being, and therefore also for the realm of the natural sciences, above and beyond empirically known laws. . . .

"For some time now, alas, science and philosophy have lived apart. It would be hard to determine what were the causes of or whose the responsibility for this harm. It is certain that the reason for this divorce does not lie in the quest itself into nature along the two roads leading to the truth. Rather, it lies in historical contingencies, and in men who were not always possessed of good will and the competence which were called for.

"Scientists came to believe in time that natural philosophy was a useless burden, and they refused to be guided by it. On the other hand, philosophers failed to keep up with scientific progress, and lingered among formalisms which they ought to have abandoned. But at a time when, as we have shown, the inescapable necessity for solid analysis, as well as for the construction of a unified synthesis, presented itself, scientists experienced the influence of philosophies which circumstances of time put at their disposal. Many of them, it may be, noticed but slowly that their research was influenced by particular philosophical tendencies....

"More than one great thinker, faced with the problems of a philosophy of science, ended in skepticism and maintained that one must be content with simple statements of fact and do no more than try to fit these into simple synthetic formulas, which, starting from the initial data, might forecast the possible operations of a physical system. This state of mind indicates renunciation of all conceptual introspection and loss of the hope of ever achieving any inspired universal synthesis. Nevertheless, we do not believe that such pessimism is justified. We think, rather, that the natural sciences, once they are in lasting touch with a critical realism such as was ever that of the *philosophia perennis,* as seen in its most distinguished representatives, can come to an over-all vision of the visible world which will in some degree satisfy man's quest and burning desire for the truth.

"One other point must be emphasized: While science has the

191

duty of seeking its own inner coherence and of taking its inspiration from a sound philosophy, never must philosophy presume to determine truths which are answerable solely to experience and the scientific method. Only experience, taken in its widest sense, can uncover, in their infinite variety, all the magnitude, all the possible laws of matter, all that the Creator has willed to exist. . . .

"You who are the interpreters of creation, be teachers eager to reveal creation's beauty, its power, its perfection, and to bring your fellow men to delight in them. Teach others to see, to understand, to love the created world, so that their admiration for such sublime splendor may bring them to their knees and draw their minds to adoration."

Christmas Greetings

and my lover came
on the day of snowbells
sundrifts
moaning in anger

so the evening set
on daily carnival
with laughter
walking o'er the river

      the morning sun
      did shine upon
      his face
      to laugh
      'What ecstasy!'
      cried my crippled heart

thus in the season of yesteryear
when winter was forever
tomorrow was today
in the season of mindlessness

thus did my latent lover come to me